Strengthen YOUR Spelling

kn wr

wh ?

-tion

-ough

-dge !

' ph -tch

-sion

?

SYS

Worksheets on spelling, phonics and punctuation

Elizabeth Wood

Hodder & Stoughton

A MEMBER OF THE HODDER HEADLINE GROUP

Also by Elizabeth Wood:

Exercise your Spelling (ISBN 0 340 52234 8)

British Library Cataloguing in Publication Data
A catalogue record for this title is available from the British Library

ISBN 0 340 66349 9

First published 1996
Impression number   10 9 8 7 6 5 4 3
Year   1999   1998   1997

Page design and make-up by Bowberry House Design, Kent, England.
Printed in Great Britain for Hodder & Stoughton Educational, the educational publishing division of
Hodder Headline Plc, 338 Euston Road, London NW1 3BH by Redwood Books, Trowbridge, Wiltshire

Contents

Introduction _____

Strengthen Your Spelling is a photocopiable resource designed to give additional spelling practice to pupils, from age 9 upwards, needing extra help with phonics and spelling rules. The revision element has been strongly emphasized. A 'rule recap' section at the end of relevant exercises recalls the rule just used, and periodic rule quizzes, reinforcing work covered in previous pages, encourage students to recall rules and phonic patterns. The exercises on each page are presented in manageable portions which, if the revision element is to be fully utilised, should be worked on separate days.

Some basic punctuation rules and exercises are included. Also, for learning sight words (words which do not follow regular spelling rules), some different methods have been introduced to encourage students to seek out the learning method for these words which suits them best.

Tracking exercises have been included with a dual purpose: to encourage observation, and also, when the tracking has been done, for use as a dictation. (For instructions on tracking see sheet 2.2.) In most exercises it has been assumed that a pupil's reading ability will be above his spelling ability, but in the tracking exercises the spelling has been kept as simple as possible.

To stimulate motivation in students who are finding spelling difficult, the exercises are varied, and puzzles (with answers) have been introduced throughout the pack.

Although each page can be used as a separate unit, there is a structured and developing sequence of difficulty through the pack; it can be used alongside, or following, the companion **Exercise Your Spelling** material, or as an independent revision book. Taken page by page, it could cover the revision of two or three years' work on spelling rules and phonics.

For teachers without easy access to copying facilities, the pages could be used repeatedly by slipping a plastic folder over a page and working the exercise with a water soluble projector marker pen.

The following diacritical marks are used throughout the book:

'–'   indicates the name, and /–/ the sound, of a letter or letters,
      e.g. 'c' can say /k/ or /s/,   a **c**lashing **c**ymbal.

ˇ   indicates a vowel,   ᶜ   indicates a consonant,
                    c c v c v
      e.g. p r i c e.

˘   shows that a vowel is short,
      e.g. ăpple, ĕgg, ĭnk, ŏrange, ŭmbrella.

‾   shows that a vowel is long,
      e.g. āpe, ēven, īris, ōpen, ūnit.

Vowels

The **five vowels** – **a**, **e**, **i**, **o**, **u** – each have a **short** and a **long** sound.

Sometimes '**y**' acts as a **vowel** in place of '**i**', e.g. sunny sky.

Every word must have at least **1 vowel**, e.g. Did Jim have Tom's gun?

The **short vowels** are:

apple , **e**gg , **i**gloo , **o**range , **u**p .

A WRITE two words with short vowels, to rhyme with each word below.

ran	jet	bin	not	bun
pan	*net*	_____	_____	_____
_____	_____	_____	_____	_____

A **long vowel** says its **name**,

  e.g. **a**pe, **e**asy, **i**ris, **o**pen, **u**niform.

To make a short vowel **long**, **add** 'e' after **1** vowel + **1** consonant,

  e.g. tap tap**e**, bit bit**e**, hop hop**e**, cut cut**e**.

B PUT a vowel in each space here to make a word. The vowel will be long.

bl__me   d__ke   sh__pe   f__ve   h__de   m__de

t__be   h__me   j__ke   c__se   g__me   n__ne

C PROOF READ this to find mistakes. ADD an 'e' if you need a long vowel.

The nam*e* of Sam's dog is Duk*e*. Sam is nin , and Tim is

fiv . As a jok , Sam put Tim's hat on Duk . This mad Tim

mad . For Duk it was a gam , but soon Tim's hat was in

bad shap . Tim ran hom to his Mum and she was cross with

Sam , but Sam said "Don't blam me , blam Duk ."

rule RE CAP

Vowel sounds can be _____ or _____ .

'e' after 1 vowel + 1 consonant makes a _____ vowel _____ .

Strengthen Your Spelling. Copyright © 1996 Elizabeth Wood. Published by Hodder & Stoughton Educational. The publishers grant permission for copies of this sheet to be made in the purchasing school or college for use solely in that institution.

Consonants: blends

> **Consonants** are all the letters in the alphabet which are **not** vowels.

> **Consonants** can **blend** together but still say
> their own sound,
>   e.g. **cr**ab, **cl**ock, **st**eps, **fr**og

A COMPLETE these words with a consonant blend. ___st___op

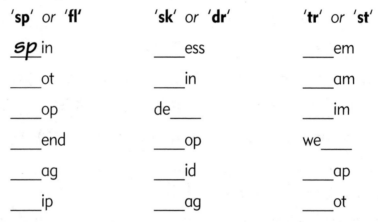

___oss   ___ee   ___ing

B MAKE words by adding:

'sp' or 'fl'	'sk' or 'dr'	'tr' or 'st'
sp in	___ess	___em
___ot	___in	___am
___op	de___	___im
___end	___op	we___
___ag	___id	___ap
___ip	___ag	___ot

C FILL each space with a word that rhymes with the word in the box.

slot	There is a ___*plot*___ to kill the king.
trip	I lost my _____ on the rock.
crab	_____ hold of my hand,
clip	then you will not_____.
free	My cat is stuck up a _____.
string	_____ me a ladder to get him down.
crop	Do not _____ that jug. It is glass.
flap	Give her a _____. She sang well.
slug	We have lost the _____ for the bath.
brink	I _____ milk.

Consonants: digraphs: 'sh', 'ch', 'th' _____

A **digraph** is **two letters** together which create a **new sound**,
e.g. **sh** **sh**ip , **ch** **ch**ip , **th** **th**is **th**in man.

A ▸ COMPLETE these words with a digraph, 'sh', 'th' or 'ch'.

ba____   ____ell   ____urch

B ▸ PUT ONE of these digraphs or consonant blends into each space:

ch, sh, th, cr, fr, lk, sl, sp, st.

Jo said "I _th_ ink I will go to the ____ops to get mi____ for my cat and
fi____ and ____ips for lun____." On her way back wi____ the ____ings in her
bag Jo ____id on a wet ____ep. She fell wi____ a cra____ and ____ilt the
mi____ and ____e fi____ and ____ips. Jo's cat was ____oss and ____at at Jo,
____en it ru____ed off to ____e steps to see if the fi____ was ____ill there,
and Jo went back to the ____op to get some ____esh mi____.

/**ch**/ at the end of a **short** word is spelt '**ch**' or '**tch**':
　'**ch**' after 2 vowels (v v) or vowel consonant (vc), e.g. ĕăch ărch,
　'**tch**' after 1 **short** vowel, e.g. hŭ**tch**,　mă**tch** .

C ▸ TRACK the words ending 'tch' like this. Keeping your pencil on the paper all
the time, START at the left-hand side and UNDERLINE all the words, CIRCLING
each 'tch' word as you pass it.

A (witch) with an (itch) fell into a ditch and got a bad scratch on her leg,
so a Dutchman lent her a crutch. She put her hand on a notch in the crutch,
and went to the end of her patch to fetch her
pets from the hutch. She had to stretch
her hand into the hutch to catch them.

Label this picture _____

sYs
2.2

Consonants: /k/: 'c' or 'k' _____

① Always use '**c**' for /k/ if you can, e.g. **c**up, **c**at;

BUT ② use '**k**' for /k/ before '**e**', '**i**' and '**y**', e.g. **k**eg, **k**it, s**k**y;

and ③ use '**k**' at the **end** of a **short** word, e.g. hoo**k**, ris**k**.

A ▶ MARK each word below with ①, ② or ③ to show which rule it is using.

clap	kept	crisp
desk	bunk	keep
fact	crab	wink
kit	skip	cut
sky	scan	camp
cup	keen	thank
look	risky	skid

B ▶ FILL IN a 'c' or a 'k' in these phrases.

drin____ from a ____up   s____ratch my bac____

____eep ____ool   a s____id in the ____ar

a thic____ s____in   ma____e a pa____t

s____an the s____y   a fris____y ____itten

he ____ept my boo____   he's ____een on ____amping

a luc____y stri____e   Can you ____oo____ me a ____ebab?

a pac____ of ____risps   don't ____ill the ____ing

rule RECAP _____

To say /k/ use '___' if you can.

BUT use '___' before '___', '___' and '___', and use '___' to end a word.

SIGHT WORDS Dan's <u>friend</u> <u>said</u>, "Can <u>you</u> <u>come</u> with us?"
WRITE each underlined word three times, saying the word, then each letter as you write it. Now CHECK. Is your spelling right?

_____ _____ _____ _____

_____ _____ _____ _____

_____ _____ _____ _____

Consonants: 'm' or 'n' mid-word; 'ng', 'nk'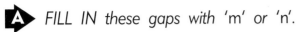

> Use 'm' before 'p' or 'b', e.g. sta**mp**, thu**mp**, nu**mb**er.
>
> Use 'n' before 'd', 't' or 'ch', e.g. ha**nd**, te**nt**, bu**nch**.

A *FILL IN these gaps with 'm' or 'n'.*

hu__t, tra__p, be__ch, spe__d, tu__ble, e__pty, spli__t,

i__ch, reme__ber, bu__p, bu__ch, sta__d, li__p, wi__d.

B *COPY this story, putting the words in the brackets in the right order.*

Pat and Jim (tent mend Jim's will) and

_____

(up camp set a) by (duck the pond).

_____

They will have (for chips ham and lunch).

_____

rule RE CAP

> Use '__' before 'd', 't' or 'ch'; '__' before 'b' or 'p'.

C *CHOOSE between 'ng' and 'nk'. CROSS OUT the word that you do not need.*

I will meet you at the skating ring/rink. Bring/Brink your skates.

There was a bang/bank as the ship bumped into the bang/bank.

Do you thing/think that this bird has hurt its wing/wink?

D *FILL IN '-ng' or '-nk'.*

A tru____ full of ju____.

A stro____ dri____.

Ha____ up that pi____ hat.

A ga____ of thugs.

Ri____ the bell.

I thi____ this thi____ sti____s!

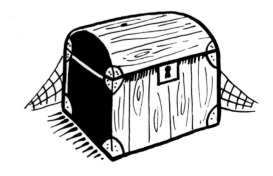

sYs
2.4

Consonants: revision

ACROSS

1 Potato c - - - - - .
5 - - - - your hat on a peg.
7 Not under.
8 A mark like a full stop.
9 A short form of 'is not'.
12 Where you can get cash.
13 Your - - - - has 5 fingers.
15 You and me. - - went out.
16 I will - - - - this to you.
19 You can write with this.
20 To finish is to - - -.
21 You get water from a - - -.
23 A lot of noise. D - -.
24 A bed for a baby.

DOWN

1 Cut with an axe.
2 A length of thin cord.
3 Part of your leg.
4 One - - - one makes two.
6 One, two, three - - .
10 A hop, a - - - - and a jump.
11 At that time.
12 I must run. I will - - late.
14 - - - - the rubbish here.
15 Seven days.
17 An animal doctor.
18 An - - - number, like three.
21 I go - - school.
22 Look - - me.

RULE QUIZ 1 ??

Which letter is sometimes used as a vowel instead of 'i'? '___'

What must every word have? A _____.

Do you use 'c' or 'k' to say /k/ before 'e'? '___'

Would you put 'm' or 'n' in 'ra...p' and 'stu...p'? '___'

Put the spelling right here: I rank the bell.

Is the first vowel long or short in 'brave' and 'kite'? _____

Capital letters, full stops. Plurals _____

> A **capital letter** is used for:
>
> ① starting a sentence, ② names of people, places or animals, ③ 'I'.

> A **SENTENCE** must have ① a **capital letter** at the beginning,
>
> ② a **full stop** at the end,
>
> ③ a **verb** (a doing word),
>
> ④ a **subject** (who or what is doing...),
>
> and ⑤ it must make complete sense.

A ▸ Some of these groups of words are sentences, some are only phrases.
TRACK the **sentences**. *PUT IN 4 capital letters and 5 full stops.*

if you do this   Sara had fish for lunch   that dog is too hot

mum has a red hat   seeing the sun   which I gave you

the old man goes to bed at ten   this is Tom's cat   to be very good

B ▸ *READ this aloud, then put in 8 capital letters and 4 full stops.*

when tod the fox got up he went to see his chum snap snap was hungry so

they went to look for a hen for dinner just as tod and snap got to the hen

run there was a bang the farmer had shot at them with his gun

> Add '**-s**' at the end to make a word **plural**,
>
> e.g. hat 🎩 hat**s** 🎩🧢 .
>
> BUT add '**-es**' when you hear an /ĕz/ ending,
>
> e.g. cross cross**es**,   bunch bunch**es**,   box box**es**.

C ▸ *ADD '-s' or '-es' to these words.*

fish___	mass___	pin___	spot___	cross___
cub___	bell___	clip___	match___	tap___
pack___	fox___	witch___	six___	crash___

*rule*RECAP _____

> Add '___' for a plural, or, if you hear /ĕz/, add '___'.

Past tense verbs '-ed' or '-t'

> **Verbs** in the **past tense** tell us that something has already happened.
> If you can say 'Yesterday I...', you need a **past tense verb**.

> For a **past tense verb**, add '-ed' to a **whole** word,
>   e.g. Jack jump**ed** a ditch, but seem**ed** to slip as he land**ed**.
> *Notice:* '-**ed**' can say /t/, e.g. jump**ed**;   /d/, e.g. seem**ed**;   /ĭd/, e.g. land**ed**.

A *SORT these verbs into sets:*

banged, hunted, bumped, mixed, melted, cracked, yelled, printed, filmed.

'-**ed**' *says* /ĭd/	'-**ed**' *says* /d/	'-**ed**' *says* /t/
_____	_____	_____
_____	_____	_____
_____	_____	_____

> For a past tense verb **without a whole word before a /t/ ending**,
> add '-**t**', e.g. 'Yesterday I... spen-**t**, lef-**t**, kep-**t**, etc.

B *PUT '-ed' or '-t' on to these starters to make a past tense verb.*
(Remember, only add '-ed' to a <u>whole</u> word.)

crash____	buzz____	lef____	arm____
kep____	land____	rush____	box____
want____	crep____	dust____	len____
miss____	help____	wep____	stamp____
call____	start____	melt____	hand____
hunt____	ben____	sort____	fill____
spen____	pick____	bang____	slep____

Now read what you have written. There are /ĭd/, /d/ *and* /t/ *endings.*

*rule*RE CAP

> Only add '____' to a <u>whole</u> word, otherwise add '____'.

Past tense verbs: '-t'

Note You need a **past tense verb** when you can say 'Yesterday I...'.
In the list below, all the words end with '-t'.
They are **nouns** (naming something) or **past tense verbs** (doing words).

A FIND the past tense verbs here by saying 'Yesterday I...',
e.g. Yesterday I <u>slept</u>. If it sounds right, it is a verb, UNDERLINE it.

<u>slept</u>	fist	vest	bent	melt	hit
rust	bit	sent	spent	felt	meant
belt	test	cart	crept	list	print
spot	punt	kept	lit	went	hint
lift	lent	tilt	pest	hunt	hurt
left	fact	net	got	west	act

B If your underlining is right, one of the underlined words should make sense in
each of these spaces. FILL IN the right letters.

You l_____ me a penny which was b_____,

And you s_____ me to the shops, so I w_____.

I s_____ money on a candle which I l_____,

I g_____ a pear, and an apple which I b_____.

The apple h_____ my teeth, so I l_____ it,

And the pear f_____ very soft, but I k_____ it.

I m_____ to buy much more but h_____ my head,

So I c_____ back to my home and s_____ instead.

SIGHT WORDS I <u>saw</u> the police. <u>Who</u> <u>were</u> <u>they</u> looking for?
WRITE each underlined word three times, saying the word then the letters.

_____ _____ _____ _____

_____ _____ _____ _____

_____ _____ _____ _____

Now CHECK. Is your spelling right?

sYs
4.2

'ar', 'or', 'er'

Say '**ar**' as in **ar**ch , '**or**' as in f**or**k , '**er**' as in f**er**n .

A JOIN two syllables to make a word, WRITE it, then FIND it here ↓ ⤡

stor	tist	_____
let	yard	_____
bor	y	*story*___
farm	der	_____
ar	ter	_____
al	ker	_____
cor	per	_____
dar	ty	_____
tem	ner	_____
for	arm	_____

f	w	c	v	s	h	a	r	p
l	a	o	s	t	e	r	n	d
c	a	r	g	o	r	t	n	a
b	c	d	m	r	b	i	s	r
f	o	r	t	y	h	s	e	k
i	r	r	b	s	a	t	p	e
s	n	r	d	m	t	r	e	r
t	e	m	p	e	r	a	d	n
v	r	a	l	a	r	m	r	z

Now find these words:
cargo, cord, herb, sharp, star, stern, verb.

Here are some clues to the syllable words above. WRITE in the answers.

Not as light: _____ An edge: _____ A tale _____

In the alphabet there are 26 _____s. In a bad _____

A square has four _____s. Hens live here: _____

A painter: _____ An _____ clock wakes you up.

Goods on a ship: _____ More than 39: _____

In parts of Britain, '**a**' before 'f', 's' or 'th' can sound like /**ar**/.

B COPY this rhyme, then underline any 'a' which **you** pronounce as /ar/.

Father's raft went rather fast, _____

But all that class went faster, _____

The pile-up at the end was vast, _____

And Father's leg's in plaster. _____

'ar', 'or', 'er': 'are', 'ore'

'e' after 'ar' changes /ar/ to /ā-er/,
e.g. I take c**are** of my car.

A READ *these words, then use them to complete the sentences:*

bare, beware, care, dare, fare, mare, scare, share, spare, stare.

I _____ not put my _____ hand over that flame.

I have lost my bus _____, may I _____ your taxi?

If you pat that _____ you will _____ her.

_____ of that dog. When you _____ at him he bites.

Take _____ of your _____ cash. You may need it one day.

B TRACK *the '-are' words here.*

"Take care on the bare rocks," Kate said, "and
beware of the crabs. They scare me when
they stare like that." Clare just said to Kate,
"I dare you to put a foot in the water."

"Oh no," said Kate, "spare me that and you can share all my chips."

'e' after 'or' does not change the sound at all, e.g. c**ore**.

C READ *these words, then* USE *them to complete the phrases below:*

bore, before, core, more, sore, shore, store, swore, tore, wore.

The sea _____. He is a _____. A _____ finger.

_____ you go. There is no _____. An apple _____.

Put it in the _____ room. He was rude. He _____.

I _____ the jacket that I _____ to school.

*rule*RE CAP

'e' ending changes the sound of '_____' but not of '_____'.

Question marks

A **question mark** (?), like a listening ear above a full stop, tells us that the speaker or writer is expecting an answer.

A **question** ① starts with a capital letter
and ② ends with a question mark.
The **answer** starts with a capital letter.

A *FILL IN 5 question marks, 3 full stops and 12 capital letters. When you find a question, ADD an answer.*

that cat's name is tom _____   did amy hang up her hat _____

is this ham for me _____   can ben sit by me _____

you did jump well _____   we will have lunch at 12 _____

must i go to school _____   is a post box red or green _____

B *SORT these sentences into the right order to make a story. Now WRITE them down, putting in capital letters, full stops and a question mark.*

and then back to mark's house for hot dogs

"shall we go for a swim" mark said

sam got on his bike and

so they went for a swim

"yes" said sam

went to see his friend mark

_____

_____

_____

_____

_____

_____

Revision

RULE QUIZ 2???

Which letter do you usually use to say /k/? ___

Which letter is used to say /k/ at the end of a short word? ___

'How does the 'a' in 'fast' sound in some areas? /____/

Is 'swam' a present or past tense verb? _____

Is 't' added to a whole word to make a past tense verb? _____

Do you find 'n' or 'm' before a 'p' or 'b'? '_____'

What does plural mean? More than _____.

How do you usually make a noun plural? _____ '_____'

How do you make a plural when you hear an /ez/ ending? Add '_____'.

READ these words. Use them to FILL IN the gaps in the story:

camp, catch, cubs, dark, fox, foxes,

friend, saw, shot, tent, they, were.

A _____ family had a den at the end of Ben's garden.

He and his _____ Anna made a _____ there

and hid in the _____ with a camera to try to _____

the _____ on film.

It was _____

but _____ _____

lucky and they _____ the

big foxes and three _____.

They got a good _____ of them all.

👀 SIGHT WORDS *FILL IN the missing letters here.*

I s__w the police. __ho w__r__ th__y looking for?

Dan's fr_____nd s_____d, "Can y_____ c___m___ with us?

Strengthen Your Spelling. Copyright © 1996 Elizabeth Wood. Published by Hodder & Stoughton Educational. The publishers grant permission for copies of this sheet to be made in the purchasing school or college for use solely in that institution.

The 'w' rules: 'wa', 'war'_____

'w' often changes the sound of the letter(s) coming after it.

/wŏ/ is usually spelt **'wa'**, e.g. sw**a**n, w**a**sp,
but notice the **'h'** in 'w**h**at', e.g. **Wha**t are you doing?

A TRACK the 'wa' words here.

The swans had a nest by the river. We went to watch them, but there was a swamp by the pond and we wandered into that and sank into the wet mud. I lost my wallet in the mud, just as a wasp stung my friend. He wanted a plaster, and I wanted a good wash. What a day!

/**wor**/ is usually spelt **'war'**, e.g. **war**ship , re**war**d,
but notice the **'h'** in **whar**f and **'wa'** saying /**wor**/ in **wa**ter.

B READ these words: war, warn, ward, reward, towards, backwards, warning, warm, swarm, dwarf, wharf, water, warden, warship.

CHOOSE one of them to go into each space here:

It was a _____ day and

a _____ of bees got into

a car going _____

the _____ to see the _____.

A _____ had put up a _____ that

the _____ was deep there, but the driver did not see it.

There is no _____ for telling me what happened next.

👀 **SIGHT WORDS** The <u>sword</u> <u>they</u> <u>were</u> looking for was in the <u>water</u>.
SAY each underlined word then the letters three times, then write it.

_____ _____ _____ _____

CHECK your spelling. Any mistakes? If so, practise the spelling again.

The 'w' rules: 'wa', 'war', 'wor' _____

Note 'wa' says /wǒ/, e.g. wasp, 'war' says /wor/, e.g. warship.

/**wer**/ is often spelt '**wor**', e.g. **wor**m , **wor**d,
but notice '**Were** you going out?', and '**o**' saying /ŭ/ in **wo**rry.

A PUT 'wor' into these spaces, *then* READ *what you have written.*

_____k is not a _____d _____th _____rying about.

The _____st thing in the _____ld is not having any _____k to do.

B *Using the 'wa', 'war', 'wor' rules, WRITE a rhyming word starting with 'w'*
below each of the words here:

splosh	cord	perks	verse
w*ash*____	w_____	w_____	w_____

follow	font	term	form
sw_____	w_____	w_____	w_____

pond	for	scotch	hurry
w_____	w_____	w_____	w_____

C *With a line JOIN each of the groups of starting letters to three of the endings*
to make three whole words.

		d	WRITE *the words you make here:*
	wa	st	_____ _____ _____
		m	
	war	ld	_____ _____ _____
		sp	
	wor	sh	_____ _____ _____
		ning	

*rule*RE**CAP** _____

After 'w', 'a' sounds like /_ˇ_/, 'ar' sounds like /____/,
and 'or' sounds like /____/.

sYs
8.2

The 'w' rules: words beginning 'wh-'_____

The words below starting with 'wh-' all come from Old English words which were used hundreds of years ago (before about AD 1150).
The spelling then was 'hw' and the 'h' was sounded before the 'w'.

A *READ these words aloud, putting /h/ before the /w/ like this: /h-wen/, to remind you to put an 'h' after the 'w' as you write them.*

what   when,   where,   which,   why,   who (w-hoo),
wheat,   wheel,   while,   whisper,   whistle,   whale (fish),
whine (complain),   whether (to do this or that).

B *PUT a 'wh-' word, asking a question, into each space.*

__What__ did he do?   _____ did he do it?

_____ did it?   _____ is he now?

_____ way did he go?   Do you know _____ he got away?

C *Plan a story using this pattern of question words:*

Who..........?   _____   e.g. Ben

Where..........?   _____   was in bed

When..........?   _____   last Christmas

What happened?   _____   He had a dream

How did it end?   _____   It all came true

D *USE the words in the boxes to complete these sentences.*

| whisper   what |
| which   when |

1   _____ of you can hear _____
     I say _____ I _____.

| white   while |
| whining   whale |

2   _____ you were _____, I
     think a _____ _____ swam by.

| whistle   where |

3   _____ did that _____ come from?

| wheel   whether |

4   I can't tell _____ this is my _____.

Inverted commas

> **Inverted commas** mark the **beginning** and **end** of a group of words which someone is actually saying. The spoken words start with a **capital letter** and end with a **full stop** or a **question mark**,
>
> e.g. Tom said, "We are going out at six o'clock."
>
> "Can I come too?" asked Amy.
>
> *Notice the sequence:*
>
> inverted commas, capital letter, punctuation mark, inverted commas.

A *WRITE down what is happening in this picture, using inverted commas:*

_____

_____

B *READ this story aloud, then see if you can put in 6 full stops, 5 pairs of inverted commas, 20 capital letters, and 2 question marks.*

when the farmer shot at the foxes, tod ran off, but snap hid when tod got back to snap he said that was lucky were you hit snap   no, and i am still hungry, said snap then snap stole a hen from the hen coop i am hungry too, said tod can i share that hen with you   no you can not, snap said, and he ran off with the hen to his den

👀 **SIGHT WORDS** <u>Does</u> your mum <u>put</u> <u>many</u> crisps in <u>your</u> lunch box?

IMAGINE the letters **d o e s** written in colours on your bedroom wall.

Can you see 'does' and say the letters if you shut your eyes?

When you open your eyes, WRITE what you saw _____ and CHECK it.

Now LEARN 'put', 'many', 'your' in the same way, then WRITE and CHECK.

_____   _____   _____

Word endings: /f/, /l/, /k/ _____

On one-syllable words ending /f/, /l/ or /k/:

> After **1 short vowel**, end with '**-ff**', '**-ll**' or '**-ck**'. NEVER use 'kk'.
>
>   e.g. Stu**ff** Ja**ck** fu**ll**.
>
> After **2 vowels** or **1 vowel + 1 consonant** end with '**-f**', '**-l**' or '**-k**',
>
>   e.g. loo**k**, fee**l**, roo**f**,   or   thin**k**, sel**f**, ow**l**.

> LEARN the 123 rule: In one-syllable words ending /f/, /l/ or /k/,
> counting from the first vowel, the last letter will be number 3.

A COMPLETE these words with a /f/, /l/ or /k/ ending.

pi_____, hee_____, cor_____, sni_____, thri_____, sel_____,

proo_____, tra_____, shar_____, foo_____, we_____, flu_____.

B CHANGE one letter each time. Make 'wool' into 'silk':

	w	o	o	l
A hammer or saw	*t*	*o*	*o*	*l*
A fee to cross a bridge				
To report something				
Tumbled down				
To make full				
Where they grind corn				
A drink from a cow				
A dress material	s	i	l	k

C USE the words in the box to fill the spaces here:

off	fell	Jack
stiff	roof	took
think	pill	luck
will	self	feel

After *Jack*_____ _____ _____ the

_____ he felt very _____ so he _____

a _____. With _____ I _____

he _____ soon _____ more him_____.

***rule*RERECAP** _____

After 1 short vowel, end with '_____', '_____' or '_____'.

After 2 vowels or 1 vowel + 1 consonant, end '_____', '_____' or '_____'.

Word endings: /s/, 's', 'ss' or 'se' _____

On a one-syllable word ending /s/:

> After **1 short vowel**, end with '-**ss**', e.g. cro**ss**, le**ss**.
>
> After **2 vowels** or **1 vowel + 1 consonant**, end with '-**se**',
>
>   e.g. goo**se**, hor**se**. (For '-**ce**' ending see p. 16.2).

> The 123 rule for a /s/ ending is: Counting from the first vowel,
>
> when 's' alone is number 3, to make a noun just add an 'e'.

A ▸ COMPLETE *these words with* '-ss' *or* '-se'.

dre_____,   hou_____,   cla_____,   hor_____,

ver_____,   ma_____,   el_____,   bo_____,

wor_____,   fu_____,   ble_____,   mi_____,

le_____,   rin_____,   sen_____,   fal_____.

Note '-s' is usually added to a word to make it plural, e.g. cats;
        '-ss' usually ends a word after one short vowel, e.g. miss

> These words end with **one 's'** after **1 short vowel**:
>   **Yes this bus plus gas is** the one for **us**, **as his** bus **has** no gas.

B ▸ COMPLETE *these words with* '-s' *or* '-ss'.

bu_____,   me_____,   dre_____,   ga_____,

cro_____,   u_____,   bun_____,   pre_____,

dog_____,   mo_____,   thi_____,   fu_____,

ha_____,   cuff_____,   bo_____,   i_____,

ye_____,   hat_____,   a_____,   pill_____.

*rule*RE CAP _____

/s/ ending. After 1 short vowel end with '_____'.

After 2 vowels or vowel + consonant end with '_____'.

Exceptions: _____ _____ _____ _____ _____

             _____ _____ _____ _____ _____

sYs
10.2

The sounds of 'al' and 'all'

Watch out for 'al' and 'all'.

> 'al' or 'all' can sound like: ① /ăl/, e.g. c**al**endar, sh**all**,
>
> ② /orl/, e.g. w**all**, h**al**t, **all**,
>
> or the 'l' may be silent ③ /or/, e.g. t**al**k, ch**al**k,
>
> or ④ /ar/, e.g. c**al**f, h**al**f.

Here is a rhyme to help you to remember the silent 'l' words:

    To find silent 'l' after 'a' keep CALM,
    It's in CHALK and TALK and STALK and WALK
    And CALF and HALF and PALM.

A *Fill in a word with 'al' or 'all' which answers each of these clues.*
Use the 123 rule. Count from the first vowel (1) to the last letter (3).

'al' sounding like /orl/	'al' with a silent 'l'
Not short... _tall_	Baby cow; part of your leg _calf_
Without hair... _____	Used on blackboards... _____
Everything... _____	A tree; part of your hand _____
Used with pepper... _____	To follow quietly; a stem _____
To tumble... _____	Two of these make a whole... _____
A shopping arcade... _____	Quiet, not excited... _____
To shout to... _____	To chat... _____
An order to stop... _____	To move step by step... _____

A place for meetings or a room in a house... _____

This can be made with bricks... _____

*rule*RE CAP

> 'al' or 'all' can sound like:
>
> /_____/, e.g. t**al**l, /_____/, e.g. r**al**ly, sh**al**l,
>
> /_____/, e.g. ch**al**k, or /_____/, e.g. p**al**m, h**al**f.

Revision

SIGHT WORDS *Look at these three words:* here, there, where.

There are four letters which they all share. CIRCLE them in each word.

USING THE CLUES, fill in each gap here: _____ are my socks?

They were _____, but they are not _____ now. _____

did they go? _____ they are. I put them _____ for you.

SOLVE this puzzle. These words will only fit into one of the spaces.

Number of letters

2	3	4	5	6
at	out	come	names	friend
do	you	does	water	
in		many	where	
so		said		
		what		
		they		

RULE QUIZ 3 ??

Does 'a' often say /ŏ/ after 'w'? _____

Is 'lent' a past tense verb? _____

Which letters often sound like /er/ after 'w'? /_____/

The 123 rule starts counting from the _____ _____.

To end a one-syllable word, how do you write:

    /k/ after a short vowel? '_____'

    /l/ after 2 vowels? '_____'

    /f/ after 1 vowel 1 consonant? '_____'

What can the /s/ ending be after 1 vowel 1 consonant? '_____'

Which of these sounds does 'al' <u>not</u> say? /ar/, /or/, /erl/,? '_____'

Apostrophes: short forms

In conversations, two words are often run together to make a short form,

e.g. I'm = I am, he's = he is, it's = it is, don't = do not.

An **apostrophe** (') shows *exactly* where letters have been left out.

LOOK at these other short forms: 's = has or is, 'll = will,

've = have, 're = are, 'd = would, hasn't = has not,

don't = do not, can't = can not, and **notice** won't = will not.

A COPY *these sentences, changing the underlined words for a short form.*

I <u>will</u> tell you where I <u>have</u> been. _____

I <u>am</u> cross. Greg <u>will</u> <u>not</u> come. _____

He <u>would</u> come if he could, _____

but he <u>is</u> away so he <u>can</u> <u>not</u>. _____

I <u>do</u> <u>not</u> think we <u>are</u> unlucky. _____

B EXPAND *these short forms into their long form.*

you've _____,   she'll _____,

hasn't _____,   don't _____,

he'd _____,   can't _____,

it's _____,   won't _____.

ruleRE CAP _____

An apostrophe is put in place of missing _____.

CO **SIGHT WORDS** sure, only, push, once.

"I'm <u>sure</u> you <u>only</u> have to <u>push</u> the button <u>once</u>."

LEARN *each sight word, then, with your eyes SHUT,*

WRITE *it in joined writing and CHECK it.*

_____   _____

_____   _____

'o' saying /ŭ/: before 'n', 'm', 'th' _____

> 'o' often says /ŭ/ before 'n' and
> sometimes before 'm' and 'th',
> e.g. inc**o**me, m**o**ther, m**o**nkey

Before printing was invented, writing was done with quill pens
which could only write in straight lines, so 'u', 'v', 'n' and
'm' all looked very alike. Writing 'o' instead of 'u' made reading easier.

A 'o' says /ŭ/ in all the words in the boxes. PUT them into the spaces.

Monday	won
son	month

some	sponge
monkey	money

ton	honey
monkey	some

done	brother
wondered	front

money	won
monkey	

none	London

Last _____ on a _____

my _____ _____

_____ _____ .

He spent it on a _____ cake, a _____ and

_____ _____ . The cake was quickly eaten

but the _____ weighed a _____ .

His _____ at the _____ door

just _____ what he'd _____ .

Jim didn't want the _____

and the _____ that he'd _____

had all been spent in _____

He had absolutely _____ .

B MAKE UP your own sentence and DRAW a picture using these words with
'o' saying /ŭ/: amongst, another, monkey, mother, nothing, onions.

_____

_____

_____

rule RE CAP _____

> 'o' can say /ŭ/ before '____', '____', and '____'.

sYs
14.1

'o' saying /ŭ/: before 'v'. The 'v' rules _____

To make 'v' easier to read:

① Never use 'uv' to say /ŭ/, **use 'ov'**, e.g. gl**ov**e.

② Never use 'vv', **always use only 1 'v'**, e.g. ri**v**er.

③ Never end a word with 'v', **end with 've'**, e.g. ha**ve**.

A USE 'v' rule words to solve this puzzle.

DOWN *to* Can you _ _ _ _ _ _ _ _ _ this word?

ACROSS

1 A kind of pigeon.

2 A large stream.

3 To shake with cold.

4 Skilful.

5 Over your head.

6 To own.

7 Not at any time.

8 To lack food.

ruleRE CAP _____

For /ŭ/ before 'v' put '___'. Never use 'vv' put '___',

Never end a word with 'v', add an '___'.

RULE QUIZ 4???

Where should an apostrophe go here? h a v e n t,   c a n t,   I m.

Can you remember the missing words in this rhyme?

To find silent 'l' after 'a' keep _____

It's in chalk and talk and stalk and _____

And calf and _____ and palm.

Is a vowel long or short when it says its name? _____.

Does 'e' after 1 vowel, 1 consonant make the first vowel long? _____.

Proof read these words: hav   shivver   luv   giv   levvel.

Revision: sight words

A *USE these words to solve the clues in this crossword puzzle:*

come, does, friend, many, once, one, only, push, said, sure, they, sword, water, were, who, you, your, oh.

ACROSS

1 A weapon used by a knight.

4 A question word. - - - did this?

6 Can you - - - - to my party?

7 He and she. - - - - have a dog.

8 Someone you like to be with.

10 Not more than. - - - - one boy came.

13 A number less than 2.

15 To shift something by pressing.

16 He spoke. He - - - - .

DOWN

2 You wash with this.

3 Not me or them but - - - .

4 You used to be. You - - - - .

5 - - - - upon a time.

9 I do, he - - - - .

11 Belonging to you.

12 To be confident. I am - - - - .

13 A cry of surprise.

14 A lot of things or people.

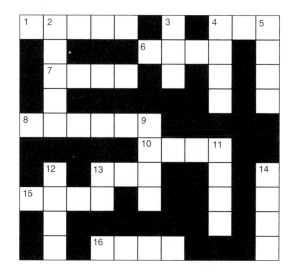

B *CAN YOU solve the pirate's message using this code?*

a	b	c	d	e	f	g	h	i	j	k	l	m	n	o	p	q	r	s	t	u	v	w	x	y	z
z	y	x	w	v	u	t	s	r	q	p	o	n	m	l	k	j	i	h	g	f	e	d	c	b	a

Q z p v   h z d   d s v i v   b l f   k f g   g s v

— — — —   — — —   — — — — —   — — —   — — —   — — —

t l o w.   Y v   h f i v   g l   n l e v r g   l m

— — — —   — —   — — — —   — —   — — — — — —   — —

g s v   m v c g   g r w v.   *signed:* z   u i r v m w.

— — —   — — — —   — — — —   —   — — — — — —

Soft 'c': before 'e', 'i', 'y'

When 'c' comes before 'e', 'i' or 'y' it is soft and says /s/,
e.g. I **cy**cle to the **ce**ntre of the **ci**ty.

A RECALLING what 'ch' says and when 'c' says /s/, READ this list.

chest	can	cycle	celery	cute	cylinder
cinema	chase	cement	coke	chapter	centre
cyclone	conduct	chin	cymbals	civic	crash
chalk	chocolate	circus	capsize	circle	certificate

READ the list again and CIRCLE each 'c' which sounded like /s/.

Note /s/ before 'e', 'i' or 'y' can be 's' or 'c', but...

Mid-word '**ce**' and '**ci**' are more usual than 'se' or 'si',
e.g. par**cel**, pen**cil**.

B FILL in 's' or 'c' here (all the gaps on one line need the <u>same</u> letter).

I always __ycle to school ex__ept when it is __old in De__ember.

The __onvict was in the __ellar in a __ell with a low __eiling.

To __ay that the __un __ets in the east is non__en__e.

__an you __ome to the __on__ert at the __ivi__ __entre?

The __ock shop __ells __triped __ocks. I'll __end __ome to Tim.

I __an't de__ide whether making s__ent is a s__ien__e.

C SOLVE these clues with one of the completed words above.

Perfume _____ The middle _____ Has for sale _____

Apart from _____ To make up one's mind _____

Chemistry is a _____ A musical event _____

The inside roof of a room _____ A prison room _____

rule RECAP

'c' before 'e', 'i' or 'y' is _____ and says /_____/.

Soft 'c': '-ce' and '-se' endings _____

> To **end** a word after a **long** vowel, **2 vowels** or **1 vowel + 1 consonant**,
> /**s**/ is more often '-**ce**' than '-se'. When in doubt use '-**ce**',
> e.g. fen**ce**, mi**ce**

A ▶ *TRACK the words ending '-se' here ('-se' is the <u>less</u> usual ending).*

The horse was loose, he slipped his noose,

And, what was worse, he met the nurse.

She didn't curse, she had more sense,

But someone else was rather tense.

Back at the house a goose gave chase,

With a girl with a purse, a boy covered in grease,

A man with false teeth and a gaggle of geese,

And all of them said 'Will this chase never cease?'

But then, in the end, the horse ran back to base,

And all ended well in this horse chasing case.

And all this, so that you will remember this verse,

And words ending 'se' won't make you all curse.

B ▶ *Now DRAW more sketches by the verse to remind you of some '-se' words.*

rule RE CAP _____

> A /s/ word ending is more often '____' than '____'.

C ▶ *FILL IN '-ce' or '-se' (use the '-ce' rule and the '-se' exceptions above).*

pla**ce**__	fen____	for____	fal____	hou____
twi____	pri____	hor____	spa____	loo____
prin____	wor____	ra____	ni____	ca____
nur____	sin____	cea____	ba____	tra____
goo____	cur____	chan____	noti____	cha____

Soft 'c': 'cce', 'cci'

> 'cc' before 'o' or 'u' says /k/, e.g. a**cc**ordion,   a**cc**use.
>
> With '**cce**' or '**cci**', the first '**c**' says /**k**/, the second says /**s**/,
>
> e.g. su**c**/**c**ess,   a**c**/**c**ident,   a**c**/**c**ept.

A CIRCLE or colour the soft 'c's, then READ the sentences here.

Alice was at that recent incident where the police came, but she is

innocent. She is sincere and honest. The man, not concentrating,

accelerated, exceeded the speed limit and had an accident.

Do you accept that 'Nothing succeeds like success'? I do.

SIGHT WORDS **nouns:** advice, practice; but **verbs:** advise, practise.

In the alphabet '**n**' for **noun** comes before '**v**' for **verb**, and '**c**' in the **nouns**

'advice', 'practice' is before '**s**' in the **verbs** 'advise', 'practise',

i.e. My advice is 'Go to games practice.' 'I advise you to practise.'

FILL the gaps: Practi___e makes perfect. Can you practi___e everyday?

RULE QUIZ 5 True or false? ???	True	False
To make a past tense verb, add '-t' to a part (not whole) word.	☐	☐
'c' says /k/ before 'e' and 'y'.	☐	☐
These are double letters which are never used: 'kk', 'v v'.	☐	☐
The sound /ŭ/ before 'v' is always spelt with an 'o'.	☐	☐
The sound /ŭ/ before 'n' is **always** spelt with an 'o'.	☐	☐
'c' starting a word before 'e', 'i' or 'y' usually says /s/.	☐	☐
'Advice' and 'practice' ending with '-ce' are nouns.	☐	☐
The sound /k/ before 'i' is spelt with a 'c'.	☐	☐
'Advise' and 'practise' ending with '-se' are nouns.	☐	☐
'-ce' is a more usual /s/ word ending than '-se'.	☐	☐
'War' often sounds like /wor/.	☐	☐

Apostrophes showing possession

Note Apostrophes can show where letters are missing, e.g. I'm good.

> An **apostrophe** can also show possession. Put it **after** the possessor,
> then **add** 's', e.g. a boy**'s** cap, the men**'s** hats.
> After a name or word ending '-s', **add an apostrophe**, but **no** extra 's',
> e.g. Jame**s'** boots, the three dog**s'** dinner.

A *ADD an apostrophe, and an 's' if needed:* the man**'s** dog

Jill____ cats   the two boys____ Mum   the children____ hands

B *TICK here once for one owner, twice for more than one owner.*
*(Remember, to find the owner, read off **before** the apostrophe.)*

The boys' bags _____   the cat's dishes _____   the men's tools _____

the ships' masts _____   the boy's books _____   the man's _____ case

C *PUT a circle round the right spelling in these phrases.*

The childrens toys   The children's toys   The childrens' toys

The man's gun   The mans' gun   The mans gun

All three dogs tails   All three dogs' tails   All three dog's tails

James' car   Jame's car   James car

> **Possessive pronouns** – my, your, her, his, our, their, its –
> do **not** have an apostrophe, e.g. his car, its legs, her hat.

D *SOLVE the clues with a possessive pronoun.* Belonging to me: __*my*__

belonging to him: _____   belonging to her: _____

belonging to you: _____   belonging to them: _____

This letter lost _____ stamp in the post.

rule **RECAP** _____

> Put an apostrophe _____ the owner(s) and add '___'.

Silent 'k' and 'w'

Some words have silent letters, such as 'k' before 'n' and 'w' before 'r'. Store these words in your mind in a sound pattern. Say the silent letter to yourself as you read the word, e.g. k-nit , w-rong.

▶ *LEARN each underlined word this way, say it 3 times, then cover and write.*
I <u>know</u> Ken <u>knocked</u> his <u>knee</u> playing football.

_____   _____   _____

Win was <u>wrong</u> to <u>write</u> the words for the test on her <u>wrist</u>.

_____   _____   _____

CHECK your spelling. Any mistakes? Have another go, then try again.

_____   _____   _____

Rule revision:

/k/, soft 'c': 'r' digraphs: endings '-e', /f/, /k/, /l/, /s/.

All these words link to a rule you have learnt. FIND THEM here. ↗↙

send	half
kept	carve
cake	cord
use	horse
kite	chalks
coke	space
desk	place
pinch	curse
cross	verse
chill	cement
fool	cylinder
dock	cinder
risk	concern
hulk	cyclone
self	wrap
cuff	knees
seek	know
lucky	wrote

```
s  p  i  n  c  h  u  s  e  b  c
p  l  a  c  e  u  s  e  e  k  y
a  u  g  h  a  l  f  l  c  l  c
c  c  r  i  s  k  g  f  o  o  l
e  k  y  l  e  d  e  s  k  w  o
c  y  h  l  c  o  n  c  e  r  n
h  c  o  m  i  k  n  o  w  o  e
a  a  r  c  i  n  d  e  r  t  k
l  r  s  o  v  e  d  t  a  e  i
k  v  e  r  s  e  o  e  p  b  t
s  e  n  d  u  s  c  u  r  s  e
c  e  m  e  n  t  k  k  e  p  t
```

Strengthen Your Spelling. Copyright © 1996 Elizabeth Wood. Published by Hodder & Stoughton Educational. The publishers grant permission for copies of this sheet to be made in the purchasing school or college for use solely in that institution.

Hard 'g', soft 'g' and 'j'

> **Hard 'g'**, /g/, is always 'g', e.g. **g**ate, **g**et, **g**ive, **g**o, **g**un.
>
> /j/ is always '**j**' before 'a', 'o' or 'u', e.g. **j**ar, **j**og, **j**ug.
>
> '**g**' is often **soft** saying /j/ when it is followed by '**e**', '**i**' or '**y**'
>
> e.g. **g**enie ⬚ , **gi**ant, **gy**mnastics.

AT THE START of a word, /j/ before 'e' or 'i' may be 'g' or 'j'. There is no rule to help. So link a word you know to one you need to learn, e.g. a **g**ood **g**iant, **J**ason's **j**ersey, a **j**umping **j**eep.

A *In this list 'g' before 'e', 'i' and 'y' is soft and says /j/. COLOUR MARK all the /j/ sounds, then READ the words ALOUD.*

energy	engage	edge	general	jerked	grumpy
gentle	giant	gypsy	jetty	geography	germ
gorgeous	jewels	genuine	gymnast	giro	generous

B *FILL IN 'g' or 'j' (in each line all the gaps need 'g' or all need 'j').*

The ___ypsy was a ___enuine ___iant. He had ___igantic feet.

___im hid a ___emmy in his ___acket and went to the ___eweller's shop.

Someone ___erked his arm. He ___umped and his knees turned to ___elly.

The ___iant is ___enerally ___enerous, but today he is ___rumpy.

In ___eo___raphy we saw a ___or___eous ___emstone from ___ermany.

___ack rushed to the ___etty in his ___eep to see the Chinese ___unk.

> Sometimes there is a '**u**' between '**g**' and '**e**' or '**i**' to keep '**g**' **hard**. The '**u**' is **silent**, e.g. **gu**ess, **gu**errilla, **gu**ide, **gu**ilty, **gu**itar, dis**gu**ise, pla**gue**, ro**gue**, va**gue**, ton**gue**, catalo**gue**, **gu**inea pig.

C *Use as many 'gu' words as you can in one or two sentences here.*

_____

_____

Hard 'g', soft 'g' and 'j': /j/ mid-word _____

Note To say /g/ always use 'g', e.g. goose, guitar ⎯⎯.

For /j/ always use 'j' before 'a', 'o' and 'u', e.g. jam, jot, jut.

BUT 'g' can also say /j/ before 'e', 'i' and 'y',

   e.g. a gentle **gi**raffe   ,   a stod**gy** book.

In the **middle** of words, always use '**g**' for /j/ before '**e**', '**i**' and '**y**'

   e.g. pi**ge**on, fra**gi**le, ed**gy**, EXCEPT when you hear /**ject**/,

   e.g. I was de**ject**ed. The sub**ject** for my pro**ject** was impossible.

A *All these blanks need /j/. FILL IN 'g' or 'j'.*

__acket	en__ine	ob__ect	a__ent
le__end	pro__ect	al__ebra	ad__ective
sub__ect	ener__y	ur__ent	in__ect

B *COMPLETE this story with 'g's and 'j's.*

This was not a __oke. It must be ma__ic. A __enie
was e__ected out of a bottle with such ener__y that he
was pro__ected into space. He was very a__itated.
He needed help ur__ently. I could not ima__ine what to
do to prevent a tra__edy. But an intelli__ent pi__eon saw
this stran__e thin__ and __umped on to the __enie's
back and they __ently floated back to the __round.

👁👁 **SIGHT WORDS** Sometimes, mid-word, 'd' can sound a bit like /j/. Store the words in
syllable sound patterns in your memory like this:

   ed-u-cate, grad-u-al, pen-du-lum, in-div-id-u-al, sol-di-er.

CAN YOU SOLVE these?   It swings to and fro _____

A bit at a time _____   Just one _____

Teach _____   An army man _____

*rule*RE**CAP** _____

Mid-word, /j/ is ___ before 'e' and 'i' except in '_____'.

Hard 'g', soft 'g': word endings _____

> To end words, /g/ is '-**g**', e.g. ba**g**, rin**g**,
>
> or sometimes '-**gue**', e.g. catalo**gue**, ton**gue**
>
> va**gue**, pla**gue**, ro**gue**, fati**gue**, intri**gue**, lea**gue**.

> **Never** end a word with '-**j**'. To end one-syllable words with /**j**/:
>
> use '-**ge**' after a **long vowel** or **vowel + consonant**,
>
>   e.g. pā**ge**, frin**ge**;
>
> use '-**dge**' after 1 **short vowel**, e.g. ba**dge**, he**dge**.
>
> *Remember:* Short vowel long ending (*dge*), long vowel short ending (*ge*).

A   *FILL IN a /j/ ending. Try a long and a short vowel to find the word.*

plun_____,   mi_____,   pa_____,   ver_____,   le_____,   sta_____,

gor_____,   hu_____,   ju_____,   ba_____,   hin_____,   do_____.

If words have **more** than **1** syllable, an /ĭj/ ending is spelt '-**age**',

   e.g. lugg**age**, cabb**age**, post**age** stamp,

   EXCEPT: knowle**dge**, cartri**dge** (dge), and coll**ege**, privil**ege** (ege).

B   *READ this story, then TRACK the words with a /j/ sound.*

A big, rather vague guy, Raj, came into college with a huge glowing orange object. He said that a gypsy by the bridge in the village gave it to him. "I guess it's magic," he said. "Get a cage for it, fast." Just then the object gave a jerk and, as it jumped free, yelled at Raj, "You've no knowledge of magic." Then it vanished in a puff of smoke.

Did you find 17 words with a /j/ sound?

*rule*RE CAP _____

> At the end of a word /g/ is spelt '_____' or '_____',
>
> /j/ is '_____' or '_____'. /ĭj/ on long words is '_____'. EXCEPT on
>
> _____   _____   _____

Using a dictionary _____

A *WRITE the alphabet on this line to help you with the exercises:*

_____

B *In each group here, RING the letter which comes* **first** *in the alphabet.*

r m s e,   s b a p,   d t e g,   w o h l,   v c f k,   n j r i.

C *In these word lists, LOOK for the first letter where the words differ,*
RING THEM, then WRITE the words in dictionary order like this:

m a (t)
m a |r| k   ___**mark**___   ___**mask**___   ___**mat**___
m a |s| k

p u n c h
p r e s s   _____ _____ _____
p o r c h

c r u m b
w r i t e   _____ _____ _____
e r u p t

n o s e
n o r t h   _____ _____ _____
n o t e

s a n g
s a n d y   _____ _____ _____
s a n k

D At the top of most dictionary pages, the word on the **left** gives you the **first**
word on the page, and the word on the **right** the **last** word.

WRITE these words on the right pages, and in the right order:

moon	mash
mend	mist
mask	mix
mood	melon

mark	mat	may	met

mile	mob	monk	mop

Now SORT these:

wax	ketchup
king	wave
knee	wrong
kebab	wrist

kale	key	kid	knit

wade	way	wren	wry

RULE QUIZ 6 ???

At the **end** of a word:

which two letters together say /j/? '____'

which two letters can sound like /id/, /d/ or /t/? '____'

with more than one syllable, how would you spell /ĭj/? '____'

At the **end** of a word with only **one** syllable:

/j/ is spelt 'dge' after _____ _____ _____

/k/ is spelt '___' after vowel + vowel or vowel + consonant

/s/ is usually '___' after one short vowel, BUT these words end

with **one** 's': _____ _____ _____ _____

_____ _____ _____ _____ _____ _____ (see sheet 10.2)

Does the 'u' in 'guess' or 'guide' say anything? _____

What does the 'u' do? It stops the 'e' or 'i' making 'g' say /____/

Would you expect to find 'm' or 'n' before 'b' and 'p'? '_____'

Which comes first in a dictionary, 'meet' or 'meat'? _____

What sound does the 'o' make in 'come', 'other' and 'London'? /ŏ/

SIGHT WORDS Try linking a word you know to one you need to learn.

If you can spell '**they**', link it to '**grey**' and '**obey**',

e.g. **they obey** the **grey** man.

to, **too**, **two**. When in doubt use '**to**', e.g. I want to go to bed.

too with 2 'o's means **more** than is wanted, e.g. **too soon**, **too moody**,

or **as well** (an extra 'o' <u>as well</u>), e.g. I'll come **too**.

'**two**' is number **2**, e.g. t-wo t-wins, or **t**wo **w**hite **o**wls.

FILL IN 'to', 'too' or 'two' *here.*

"Can you take _____ more children _____ school in your car?"

"No that is _____ much _____ ask. I have _____ many already."

Exclamation mark (!); commas in interrupted sentences ___

Punctuation marks make it easier to understand what we are reading.

An **exclamation mark** tells us that a word or sentence must be read with a lot of feeling, such as surprise, alarm, urgency, disgust and so on.

 READ these sentences aloud as they are punctuated. Use a flat tone before a full stop – but plenty of feeling before an exclamation mark!

Be quiet or you will wake the baby.
I've spilt the milk. Help me mop up.

Be quiet! You'll wake the baby!
Help! I've spilt the milk!

If a sentence is interrupted, **commas** tell us where to pause,

    e.g. **Nicki**, as she was crossing the street, **slipped and cut her knee.**

The main sentence is **'Nicki slipped and cut her knee'**, but it has been interrupted by 'as she was crossing the street'. To help us with the reading, **commas** mark the start and end of the interruption.

 TRACK the interrupting phrases, COPY the sentence and ADD 2 commas.

The Queen as you know lives in London.

_____

My Mum to save time takes the bus into town.

_____

Jane's dog the smallest in the show took first prize.

_____

CHECK! If you leave out the words between the commas, do you still have a sentence that makes complete sense?

C *PUNCTUATE this:* wow sara in her new dress looks great

    and this: go home at once tom shouted at the dog the dog

        with its tail between its legs slunk away

Strengthen Your Spelling. Copyright © 1996 Elizabeth Wood. Published by Hodder & Stoughton Educational. The publishers grant permission for copies of this sheet to be made in the purchasing school or college for use solely in that institution.

Long /ā/: 'ai', homophones

Note A long vowel says its name, e.g. <u>a</u>pe, <u>e</u>at, <u>i</u>vy, <u>o</u>pen, <u>u</u>nit.

A **long** vowel needs **another vowel near**, either v + v or v + consonant + v,
e.g. b**ō<u>a</u>**t,   **ē<u>e</u>**l,   or **ō**pen, p**ā**per.

Long /ā/ can be spelt:

① with a final silent 'e', e.g. c**a**k**e**, dict**a**t**e**, rel**a**t**e**;

② with a second vowel, '**ai**' or, to end a word, '**ay**' e.g. r**ai**ny d**ay**;

③ occasionally, with '**ei**' or '**ey**', e.g. v**ei**n (for blood), th**ey**.

A *Some words which sound the same, have two different meanings and two different spellings. Can you circle the right answer for each clue?*

A MALE is a...   mallet, magic, man, mother, magnet

MAIL is...   lists, logs, lessons, lodges, letters

A SALE is in a...   shape, shovel, ship, shop, shell

A SAIL is on a...   shoot, short, shin, ship, shave

Water drops are...   rate, rail, race, rain, rage

A horse has a...   rain, raft, raid, ramp, rein

To REIGN is to...   rule, rude, rush, ruck, ruin

B *TRACK the 'ai' words in this story. Can you find 17?*

Tom and Ben were a pair of fair haired twins. They set out in their boat, to

sail to the mainland to get their mail. It began to rain and hail, but they

were not afraid. A tail wind soon took them ashore.

"I've got the mail," said Tom, "so that trip was not in vain."

"We did it," Ben said, "we didn't fail. Now we must sail home again."

rule RECAP

/ā/ can be '___'-'___' e.g. made;   '___' e.g. main;   '___' e.g. may;
'___' e.g. rein;   '___' e.g. obey.

Long /ā/: 'ai', 'ay', 'ei'

Note Long /ā/ can be: 'a-e', 'ai', 'ay', 'ei', 'ey'.

A *CHANGE, ADD or DROP 1 letter each move to solve this with 'ay' words.*

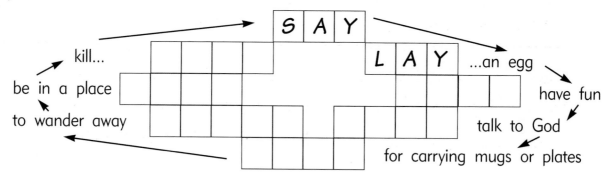

kill...
be in a place
to wander away

S A Y

L A Y   ...an egg

have fun
talk to God
for carrying mugs or plates

B *READ these words ALOUD: 'ei', 'eig', 'eigh', and 'aigh' all say /ā/.*

eight, eighteen, eighty, foreign, freight (*cargo*), neighbour,
neigh (*like a horse*), reign (*a king's rule*), rein (*a strap*), reindeer,
sleigh (*sledge*), straight, vein (*for blood*), weighing, weight.

C *SOLVE this puzzle with 'ei' and 'ai' words.*

The down clue for * to * is: Using scales to measure heaviness.

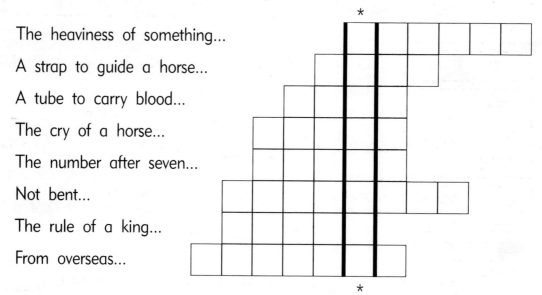

The heaviness of something...

A strap to guide a horse...

A tube to carry blood...

The cry of a horse...

The number after seven...

Not bent...

The rule of a king...

From overseas...

*WRITE 'straight' and 'weight' on a piece of paper, outlining the letters like
this:* s̲t̲r̲a̲i̲g̲h̲t̲ w̲e̲i̲g̲h̲t̲ *noticing the pattern of tall and tailed letters.
Put the paper in your pocket and each time you put your hand in your
pocket, look at the words and learn them. When you can spell them without
looking, tear up the paper and throw it away!*

Long /ē/: 'ee', 'ea'

> Long /ē/ can be spelt:
> ① 'ee', e.g. tree, wheel, knee ;
> ② 'ea', e.g teapot, leaf, seat;
> ③ 'e-e' sometimes, e.g. here, these, complete, gene.

There is no rule to help you to decide whether to use 'ee' or 'ea'.
When in doubt, try writing a word both ways and see which looks right,

e.g. eat ~~eet~~, ~~grean~~ green. If still in doubt, *USE A DICTIONARY*.

A *TRACK the 'ee' words here. Can you find 13?*

A farmer was free-wheeling down a steep hill in his jeep. He needed to see
if his sheep had been fed. Three sheep were on their feet and took to their
heels, but one was fast asleep, too full of food to move.

DRAW an 'ee' memory jogger sketch of this story on a separate sheet of paper.

B *PUT the 'ea' words in the boxes into the right spaces.*

read	real
teach	

Alex will _____ you to _____ _____ books.

heal	leave

That graze will _____ , if you _____ it alone.

beat	team
heats	reach
leading	

This is the _____ _____ . If they _____ all
the rest in the _____ , they'll _____ the finals.

each	leaves
leaf	heap

Make a _____ of _____ here. In time _____
_____ will rot down into good compost.

seals	sea
please	

_____ may we go to the _____ to watch _____ .

cheats	sneak
speak	

I will not _____ to that _____ . He _____ .

rule RE CAP

Long /ē/ can be spelt '____', '____', or '____-____'.

sYs 24.1

Long /ē/: 'ee', 'ea', homophones _____

Note Long /ē/ can be spelt **'ee'**, **'ea'** or **'e-e'**, e.g. s**ee**, t**ea**, **E**ve.

A *Some words sound the same, but their meanings and their spellings are different. LINK THESE CLUES to the right spelling with a line and a circle, like this (use a dictionary if you need to).*

A flea   a metal   a spool for thread

flee

meet   skin of an apple

meat

peel   take someone else's things

A peal of

real   animal flesh   (bites)

reel   come face to face

steel   run away

steal   not fake   bel'

B *PUT 'ea' or 'ee' into each space. (All these words are on sheet 24.1.)*

The games t**_ea_**m wanted to s____ some r____l s____ ____ ____ went off in the j____p to the s____shore. The track was st____p, but the wh____ls held fast. There were sh____p near the foot of the cliffs ____ting the gr____n grass there, but they n____ded to r____ch the end of the bay to s____ s____ls. Their f____t sank into the soft sand and their h____ls got sore, but they r____ched their target. On a h____p of rocks thr____ s____ls were asl____p, and others were out at s____. They did not want to l____ve, but the t____m were pl____sed to have b____n able to s____ s____ls.

Long /ē/: 'ea' saying /ē/ or /ĕ/ _____

'**ea**' can say   /ē/, e.g. str**ea**m, s**ea**t 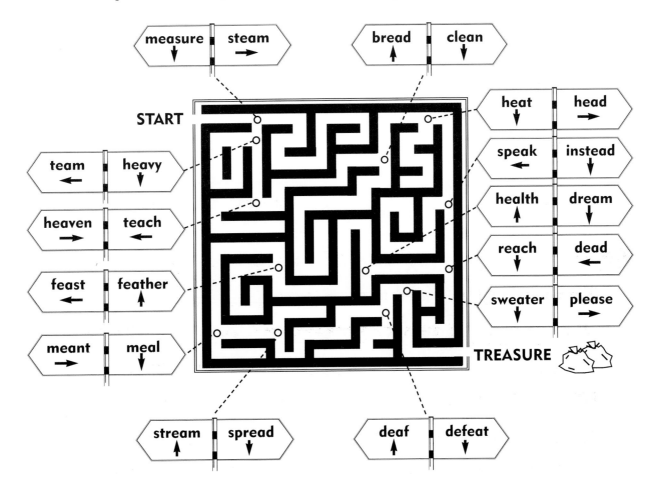,

/ĕ/, e.g. f**ea**ther ✐, br**ea**d,

and sometimes /ā/, e.g. gr**ea**t big st**ea**k.

A *On each signpost in this maze there is one word where 'ea' says /ē/,*
*and one where 'ea' says /ĕ/. CIRCLE each word with a **short** /ĕ/ sound.*
Following the arrows by these words will lead you to the treasure.

| measure ↓ | steam → |

| bread ↑ | clean ↓ |

START

| heat ↓ | head → |

| speak ← | instead ↓ |

| team ← | heavy ↓ |

| heaven → | teach ← |

| health ↑ | dream ↓ |

| reach ↓ | dead ← |

| feast ← | feather ↑ |

| sweater ↓ | please → |

| meant → | meal ↓ |

TREASURE

| stream ↑ | spread ↓ |

| deaf ↑ | defeat ↓ |

B *The words you have circled above are the answers to the clues below.*

Well-being: _____   Find the length of: _____

In the sky: _____   Lay out flat: _____

Covering a bird: _____s   In place of: _____

At the top of your body: _____   Hard to lift: _____

Not able to hear: _____   Food made from wheat: _____

Jumper: _____   Intended: _____   Not alive: _____

Long /ī/: 'igh', 'ie', 'y' _____

> Long /ī/ can be:
>
> ① 'i-e', e.g. sl**i**d**e**, br**i**d**e**, s**i**z**e**, tw**i**c**e**;
>
> ② 'igh', e.g. l**igh**t, f**igh**t, h**igh**, s**igh**, and notice the hidden '**e**' in h<u>e</u>**igh**t;
>
> ③ 'ie' or 'y' at the end of a word, e.g. t**ie** 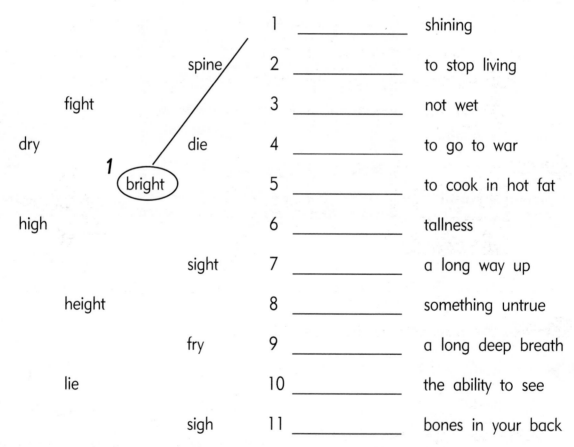, sp**y**.
>
> EXCEPTIONS ending with 'i': taxi, spaghetti, confetti.

A COVER the clues on the right and NUMBER the words in DICTIONARY order. (When all the other letters match, the shorter word comes first, i.e. 'hat' comes before 'hate'.)

B DRAW a ring round each word. Then draw a line to show it in dictionary order.

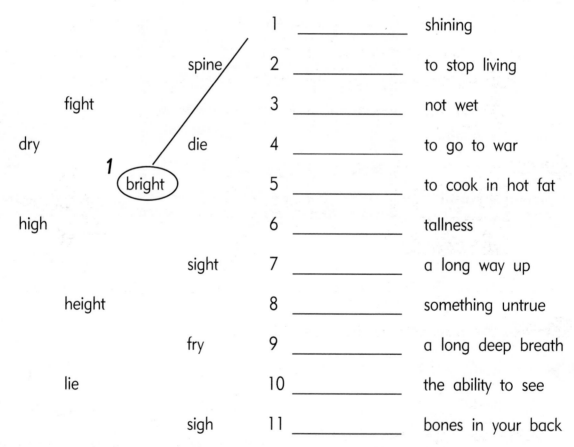

	spine	1	_____	shining
fight		2	_____	to stop living
dry	die	3	_____	not wet
1 (bright)		4	_____	to go to war
		5	_____	to cook in hot fat
high		6	_____	tallness
	sight	7	_____	a long way up
height		8	_____	something untrue
	fry	9	_____	a long deep breath
lie		10	_____	the ability to see
	sigh	11	_____	bones in your back

C CHECK that the words and clues match, then WRITE the words on the list.

rule RE CAP _____

> /ī/ can be spelt '___-___', '_____', and to end a word '_____' or '_____'. EXCEPTIONS: _____ _____ _____.

Strengthen Your Spelling. Copyright © 1996 Elizabeth Wood. Published by Hodder & Stoughton Educational. The publishers grant permission for copies of this sheet to be made in the purchasing school or college for use solely in that institution.

Long /ī/: 'i' on its own _____

Note Usually a long vowel needs another vowel near, e.g. tie, feet.

> In these words 'i' by itself is long, saying /ī/: behind, bind, blind, child, find, grind, kind, mind, rind, wild, wind.

A USE the words to FILL the gaps in these phrases: _____ the step;

a _____ animal; a 5-year-old _____; _____ corn;

_____ the treasure; ; a _____ of dinosaur

orange _____; _____ the shed; a _____ man;

_____ up the clock; _____ up a cut finger.

C SIGHT WORDS **sign**, **design**, **resign**. A way of remember a hidden 'g'.

Look at 'signal': a si**g**n is a si**g**-nal telling you to stop or to go.

or at 'signature: si**g**n your si**g**-nat-ure here ....

Try these memory joggers: The desi**g**n of this si**g**nal is good,

or 'Before you resi**g**n please si**g**n your si**g**nature here.'

B USE the sight words to label these pictures.

_____ _____ _____

C FIND the pairs of matching words, then WRITE them.

wild

design   high   mind

light   sigh   spy   resign   child

cry   height   fight

kind

_____ _____

_____ _____

_____ _____

_____ _____

_____ _____

The odd word is _____ _____ _____

Long /ō/: 'oa', 'ow'

Long /ō/ can be:	① 'o'-'e', e.g. n**o**s**e** , j**o**k**e**;
	② 'oa', e.g. b**oa**t, s**oa**k, cr**oa**k;
	③ 'ow' at the end of words, e.g. cr**ow** .

A READ these words. CONNECT each starred * word to its picture like this:

loaf*, throat, oats, coal*, afloat, boat*, boast, goat*,

oak*, soak, toad*, load, road*, goal*, foal*, moat*, soap.

B USE the 'oa' words above to complete the sentences below.

A g**oat**____ afl**oat**____ in a b_____ on a m_____.

A l_____ of c_____ held up by a t_____ on the r_____.

A mare eating o_____, and her f_____ with a sore thr_____.

A lady under an o_____ tree, with a l_____ of bread for lunch.

A team that always b_____s about the g_____s they scored, whilst

they s_____ in a hot bath with a tablet of s_____ after the game.

C TRACK 'ow' saying /ō/ here.

When the wind blows the snow into drifts, I know that you will not be slow

to throw snowballs at me. But did you know that below the snow things are

starting to grow. Let me show you a row of snowdrops.

| **rule**RE CAP |
| /ō/ can be spelt: '____-____', '____' or '____'. |

Long /ō/: 'o' on its own _____

Note Usually a long vowel needs another vowel near, e.g. c**o**ke, b**oa**t.

In some words '**o**' by itself is long (saying /ō/), e.g. gh**o**st.

FILL these gaps with words from the boxes (all the 'o's are long).

cold	hold
told	scold

I won't _____ you, but I _____ you that fingers
get _____ if you _____ on to a snowball.

host	post
ghost	both

The _____ and a guest at the party _____ saw
a _____ standing by the gate-_____.

old	almost
sold	gold

The _____ man has _____ _____ all of
his _____.

yolk	folk
most	

_____ _____ like the _____ of an egg.

close	bold
colt	bolt

That _____ is not very _____. He may
_____ if you get too _____.

SIGHT WORDS broad, and words where 'oar' says /or/.

'**broad**' has **only 1 'r'**. *Remember:* This is a **broad** road for a **B road**.

In these words 'a' is silent, 'oar' says /or/: o**ar**, ho**ar**d, bo**ar**d, cupbo**ar**d, co**ar**se, ho**ar**se, ro**ar**. *MATCH them to these clues.*

Having a croaking throat _____ Rude or not fine _____

A flat bit of wood _____ A place to store things _____

A secret store of things _____ Used for rowing _____

The sound a lion makes _____

B *LEARN this:* We took on BOARD our treasure HOARD,
But lost the OAR. Skip gave a ROAR.
His throat was HOARSE, and what he said was rather COARSE.

Long /ū/, /o͞o/, /o͝o/

| Long /ū/ can be: | ① 'u'-consonant-'e', e.g. c**u**be, c**u**re; |
| mid-word | ② '**oo**' or '**ou**', e.g. t**oo**th, s**ou**p, b**oo**k, f**oo**t; |

and notice the hidden *l* in sh**ou**ld, c**ou**ld and w**ou**ld;

| ending words | ③ '**ew**' or '**ue**', e.g. dr**ew**, cl**ue**; |
| and sometimes | ④ '**ui**', e.g. fr**ui**t, br**ui**se, s**ui**t, j**ui**ce. |

 SORT *these into sentences (the capital letters and full stops help).*

a school. This view is my good of

This is a good view of my school.

stews good. mum's true, It's my are

_____

new help you Can me boots? some choose

_____

group knew was youth I afternoon. this that

_____

tube away. I empty threw glue the

_____

sure Are pure? this you that water is

_____

 TRACK *the words with 'ew' in them.*

The wind blew, filling the new sail, and the
ship flew over the sea. But the wind grew too
strong and threw a few of the crew on to the
deck. They knew then that they must take
in the sail, and wait for news that the storm
was over. Meanwhile the crew made a strong brew of tea.

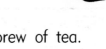

Long /ū/, /o͞o/, /o͝o/

A *FIND more words with the /ū/ or /o͞o/ sound by solving the code here:*

Code	1	2	3	4	5	6	7	8	9	10	11	12
Letter	b	c	e	f	h	i	j	o	r	s	t	u

A fellow once went on a 2 9 12 6 10 3 _ _ _ _ _ _

Dressed up in a 10 12 6 11 _ _ _ _ and smart 10 5 8 3 10 _ _ _ _ _.

When he asked for some 7 12 6 2 3 _ _ _ _ _

And a basket of 4 9 12 6 11 _ _ _ _ _,

His 10 5 8 3 _ _ _ _ slipped. All he got was a 1 9 12 6 10 3 _ _ _ _ _ _.

B *Can you FILL IN these spaces now?*

'ui' says /o͞o/ in _____, _____, _____, _____,
_____; 'oe' says /ū/ in _____.

C *FIND pairs of words that rhyme. TICK them and WRITE them down.*

_____ _____   stew pool

_____ _____   blue fruit book   _____ _____

_____ _____   wood drew fool bruise   _____ _____

_____ _____   cube took sure soup cruise   _____ _____

_____ _____   spoon huge stood clue   _____ _____

_____ _____   group soon pure   _____ _____

    suit tube

    The odd word is _____

ruleRECAP

Long /ū/ or /o͞o/ may be '__-__', '____', '____',
'____', '____', or '____', e.g. use, cool, soup, few, cue, juice.

Revision

RULE QUIZ 7 ???

True or false? Mark each of these statements true or false.

                                                                   True False

1 A short vowel says its name .... ☐ ☐

2 'gi' in the middle of a word says /jĭ/ .... ☐ ☐

3 Hard 'g' says /g/ as in 'game' .... ☐ ☐

4 'gue' at the end of a word says /j/ .... ☐ ☐

5 Mid-word, /j/ before 'e' or 'i' is 'g' except in '-ject' .... ☐ ☐

With a line, link these word endings to their sounds:

ow   y   ay   ew   ge

/ā/   /j̄/   /ū/   /ō/   /ī/

Now match these mid-word letters to their sounds:

igh   ei   g(a)   ui   ai   g(i)   oa

/ā/   /ē/   /ī/   /ō/   /g/   /j/   /ū/

Does a long or a short vowel usually have another vowel near? _____

If two vowels are together, does the first or second say its name? _____

PUNCTUATE this story using capital letters, full stops, apostrophes, inverted commas, a question mark, an exclamation mark and commas.

it was a sunny day in june and everyone was outdoors jason who was

amys friend said i wish we could go swimming

amy said i am sure mum will take us to the

pool lets go and ask her so they ran down the

road to amys house amys mum who had just

come in was drinking a cup of tea

mum can we go swimming amy asked

oh amy thats a great idea her mum said we will all go so they picked up

their swim suits and towels and they all went off to the pool

Prefixes. Word-building with syllables _____

> A **prefix** is a syllable put before a word to change its meaning,
> e.g. lucky **un**lucky,   pack **un**pack,   fresh **re**fresh,   fit **re**fit.
> These are all **prefixes**: con-,   ad-,   ex-,   in-,   dis-,   at-,   un-.

A *USE one of the prefixes above each set to complete the words below:*

'con-' *or* **'ad-'**	**'ex-'** *or* **'in-'**	**'dis-'** *or* **'in-'**	**'at-'** *or* **'un-'**
____vice	____sect	____cuss	____just
____mit	____it	____miss	____well
____vict	____sult	____vade	____tend
____dress	____pect	____dex	____do
____tent	____plain	____tress	____tempt
____nect	____vent	____fect	____tack

> When a word has more than 1 syllable, **each syllable** has a **vowel**.
> e.g. buc/ket, lem/on, hel/i/cop/ter  .

B *PUT these syllables together. TICK the word that matches the picture.*

mag-got   lim-it   win-ter

mag-net   lim-ping   win-dow

C *FIND a syllable which will end the first word, and start the second.*

A man-made substance...plas_____ _____ket   *You need this on a bus.*

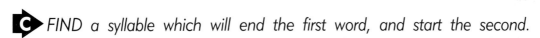   trum_____ _____rol   *This goes into a car.*

Unexpected...   sud_____ _____tist   *He checks your teeth.*

   rab_____ _____ten   *Tim was ... by a dog.*

This attracts iron   mag_____ _____ball   *A team game.*

   drin_____ _____dom   *Land where a king rules*

Suffixes: the doubling rule

A **suffix** is an ending **added** to a word to alter its meaning a little,
  e.g. fish fish**ing**,   ship ship**s**.
Vowel suffixes begin with a **vowel**, e.g. -**a**ble, -**e**d, –**e**r, -**e**st, -**i**ng.
Consonant suffixes begin with a **consonant**, e.g. -**f**ul, -**l**y, –**m**ent, -**s**.

Note 'e' after 1 vowel + 1 consonant makes the first vowel long,

  e.g. tŭb tūbe,   wĭn wīne .

A **vowel suffix** after 1 vowel + 1 consonant would also lengthen a vowel.

So: when a one-syllable word ends 1 (short) vowel + 1 consonant,
double the consonant before a **vowel** suffix to keep the vowel **short**,
  e.g. ba**t** ba**tt**ing,   thi**n** thi**nn**er.

A ADD words and endings together. You will need these extra letters:
b,   d,   ~~m~~,   n,   p,   p,   t,   t.   CROSS them out as you use them.
Remember: only double the consonant after 1 vowel + 1 consonant.

slim + est	*slimmest*	climb + able	_____
jump + er	_____	slip + ing	_____
seem + ed	_____	skid + ed	_____
hot + er	_____	high + est	_____
float + ing	_____	rain + ing	_____
stop + ed	_____	fat + er	_____
help + er	_____	tin + ed	_____
cool + est	_____	rub + er	_____

CHECK for 2 consonants between each short vowel and the added vowel.

rule RECAP _____

In a one-syllable word ending 1_____ + 1_____,
double the consonant before a _____ suffix.

Strengthen Your Spelling. Copyright © 1996 Elizabeth Wood. Published by Hodder & Stoughton Educational. The publishers grant permission for copies of this sheet to be made in the purchasing school or college for use solely in that institution.

Suffixes: drop 'e' rule

> **Note** The added '-e' in: bĭt bīte, măd māde, and hŏp hōpe, makes a **short** vowel **long**. Any vowel or '-**y**' can do this.

> So **drop the 'e'** at the end of a word **before** adding '**y**' or a **vowel** that can do the 'e's job, e.g. mak¢ + er = maker, laz¢ + y = lazy.
> **Keep the 'e' before a consonant**, e.g. hope + less = hopeless.

A *TRY these word sums.*

joke + er	*joker*	grate + ful	_____
name + ed	_____	type + ist	_____
hope + less	_____	shine + y	_____
bake + er	_____	froze + en	_____
spite + ful	_____	ice + y	_____
safe + ty	_____	love + ly	_____
use + able	_____	nine + ty	_____

ruleRECAP

Drop the 'e' at the end of a word before a _____ suffix.

B *SOLVE this puzzle using the 'doubling' and 'drop e' suffixing rules.*

Covered with ice...

Someone who makes things...

Working out a plot...

Someone who robs...

Putting oil into something...

More than one vice...

Something that itches is this...

The most nice...

Past tense of grip...

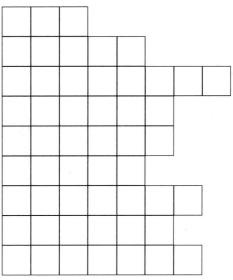

*Fill in the word between * and * here:* Your spelling is _____

Suffixes: after 'ce' and 'ge'

Note At the end of a word, 'ce' says /s/, 'ge' says /j/.
'e', 'i' and 'y' can make 'c' and 'g' soft, 'a' and 'o' cannot.

Suffixing after **'ce'** or **'ge'**:

keep 'e' before **'a'**, **'o'** or a **consonant**,

    e.g. orang**e**ade,   courag**e**ous,   manag**e**ment.

drop 'e' before **'e'**, **'i'** or **'y'**,

    e.g. rac~~e~~ + **ed** = raced,   rag~~e~~ + **ing** = raging,   spic~~e~~ + **y** = spicy.

A *ADD these words and suffixes together.*

replace + able _____   outrage + ous _____

manage + ment _____   orange + ade   _____

notice + ing   _____   lace + y   _____

Note Past tense verbs add 'ed' to whole words, 't' to part words.

B *PROOF READ this. Check suffixes with the 'double' and 'drop e' rules.*

The rober crept into the bank basment and found the lokked safe. It
was riskey, but he could blow the lock. He sliped
his rechargable torch into his pocket, and, with
gloves on, he managed to pack gelignite into the
lock, silenceing it with his coat. He lit the

fuse and steped back. There were no traceable finger prints and the bang
was silenced, but his movment had startid the alarm. He rusht out to the
street empty handed and bumpt into a policeman. "You're comeing along
with me", he said. The robber's plan had faild.

Did you find 14 mistakes?

ruleRE**CAP**

After 'ce' or 'ge' _____ 'e' before 'e', 'i' or 'y',

_____ 'e' before adding 'a', 'o' or a consonant.

Suffixes: change the 'y' rule _____

Note Almost **no English word ends** with '**i**'. End with '**-y**'.

> Before adding any suffix, **change 'y'** to '**i**', e.g. try + ed = tried,
> EXCEPT ① **keep 'y'** if a **vowel** comes **before** 'y', e.g. enjŏyed;
> ② **keep 'y'** if '**i**' comes **after** 'y', e.g. trying, applying
> (never use 'ii' except in 'skiing');
> and ③ **change 'y'** to '**ie**' before adding 's', e.g. tries. applies.

A *Add these endings to each word below:*

	-ed	**-ing**	**-able**	**-s**
copy	*copied*	*copying*	*copiable*	*copies*
enjoy	_____	_____	_____	_____
quarry	_____	_____	_____	_____
play	_____	_____	_____	_____
rely	_____	_____	_____	_____

B *Can you add three different suffixes to each of these words?*

chop	cry	buy	laze	shop
chop	_____	_____	_____	_____
chopper	_____	_____	_____	_____
chopped	_____	_____	_____	_____

C *The gaps here can be filled using the root words in B with a suffix.*

There once was a ____*lazy*____ town _____

Who said, "I want wood for my fire,

If I've got to start _____

I'd rather go _____

I'll not chop, I will buy, I'm a _____.

rule RECAP _____

> Change 'y' to '_____' before a _____
>
> except when there is a _____ before 'y' or '___' after 'y'.

sYs
30.4

Plurals: after 'f', 'fe' and 'o'

Note To form a plural add '-s', e.g. leg legs.

BUT add '-es' ① if you hear an /ĕz/ ending, e.g. crosses;

and ② **after** changing 'y' to 'i', e.g. tries, skies.

These words form their plural by changing **'f'** or **'fe'** to **'ves'**:

life, knife, wife, half, calf, scarf, elf, self, shelf,

hoof, leaf, loaf, thief and wolf,

e.g. loaf loa**ves**, half 🍎 hal**ves** 🍎🍎 .

Other words ending with 'f' **keep** the 'f' and add 's'

e.g. cliffs, roofs.

A WRITE the plurals of these words.

leaf _____	puff _____	chief _____
sniff _____	shelf _____	self _____
loaf _____	roof _____	half _____
wolf _____	thief _____	calf _____
brief _____	scarf _____	hoof _____

The words below ending with **'o'** add **'es'** for a plural:

There are no **vetoes** against **heroes**

who are exploring **volcanoes**, having

potatoes and **tomatoes** for lunch.

Other words ending with 'o' just add 's', e.g. pianos, radios.

B WRITE the plural form of these words.

solo _____	potato _____	trio _____
volcano _____	studio _____	hero _____
cello _____	tomato _____	soprano _____

Plurals: plural nouns_____

Note Add 's' or 'es' to make a noun plural, e.g. cat**s**, box**es**, ski**es**.

> A few **plural nouns** do **not** end with 's' but still take a **plural verb**, e.g. These <u>children</u> **are** good.

A *Here are some **plural** nouns. WRITE the singular form.*

children _____   men _____   sheep _____

women _____   teeth _____   geese _____

mice _____   feet _____   salmon _____

B *FIND the odd word. TICK the pairs of rhyming words, then WRITE them.*

cuffs

hooves   halves

shelves   rides   beliefs

caves   volcanoes   knives   proofs

themselves   roofs   loves   brothers   puffs

smothers   slides   cliffs   slaves

gloves   calves   grooves

sniffs   chiefs

wives

_____ _____   _____ _____

_____ _____   _____ _____

_____ _____   _____ _____

_____ _____   _____ _____

_____ _____   _____ _____

_____ _____   _____ _____

The odd word is _____

Strengthen Your Spelling. Copyright © 1996 Elizabeth Wood. Published by Hodder & Stoughton Educational. The publishers grant permission for copies of this sheet to be made in the purchasing school or college for use solely in that institution.

sYs
31.2

Plurals: collective nouns

Note Plural nouns take a plural verb, e.g. Those sheep **are** sleeping.
Nouns naming **groups** of people or things are called **collective nouns**.

> **Collective nouns** take a **singular verb**, e.g. my **team** has won,
> a **flock** of sheep **is** on the road.

A *With a line, LINK the collective nouns and words that go together.*

gaggle	bees	pride	soldiers
shoal	ships	flock	witches
herd	footballers	pack	pupils
of		of	
swarm	cows	troop	lions
team	fish	class	sheep
fleet	geese	coven	wolves

> These **pronouns**, like collective nouns, take a **singular verb**: **each**, **either**,
> **neither**, **anybody**, **nobody**, **everybody**, **everyone**, **everything**,
> e.g. **neither** of the boys **is** here.

B *FILL IN 'is' or 'are' here.*

Everyone _____ going on the same bus. Nobody _____ going by car.

Gas men _____ trying to read the meters, but the women _____ out.

The fleet _____ in port. The mice on the ships _____ a nuisance.

My teeth _____ in good shape, but my feet _____ killing me.

This class _____ the best. Each of the pupils _____ doing well.

A swarm of bees _____ flying over the field where the children _____.

A herd of cows _____ in the field where the cub pack _____ camping.

Everything _____ under control. Either way _____ right.

ruleRECAP

Collective nouns take a _____ verb.

Commas replacing 'and's

In a list, a **comma** can replace all the 'and's EXCEPT the last one:

e.g. 'Ben **and** Rupa **and** Pat **and** Jill **and** Sam are all here' becomes

'Ben**,** Rupa**,** Pat**,** Jill **and** Sam are all here'.

A *USE COMMAS in the same way to simplify this sentence.*

The National Lottery numbers were 4 and 7 and 19 and 27 and 31 and 39.

_____

Sometimes '**and**'s link a **list** of short **sentences** together,

e.g. She switched on the light **and** she went into the study **and** she

opened the computer **and** she started to play a game.

B *CROSS out the 'and's that you do not need, put in two commas and then RE-READ the sentence. Does it read more smoothly?*

All the actions are being done by the same person, so the sentence can be

simplified even more if we do **not** repeat the subject 'she'.

CROSS out the repeated 'she's and READ the sentence again.

If it **sounds** right, WRITE it here:

_____

_____

C *SIMPLIFY this sentence, deleting unneeded words and putting in commas.*

The car was going too fast and it
swerved to one side and it hit the
kerb and it knocked down a lamp post.

_____

_____

***rule*RE CAP** _____

A _____ can be used in a _____ to replace all repeated
'and's except the _____ one.

Revision. Sight words

Does a prefix come at the start or end of a word? _____

Would you find 'm' or 'n' before 'd', 't' or 'ch'? _____

Is '-ce' more usual than '-se' for a /s/ ending? _____

Does 'g' say /g/ or /j/ in 'giant'? /____/

MARK each of these statements true or false.

	True	False
This is the right way to spell 'knowledge'	☐	☐
'ea' can say /ē/ or /ĕ/	☐	☐
'ee' can say /ĕ/	☐	☐
In 'child' and 'kind' the 'i' is long	☐	☐
'Salt' comes before 'pepper' in the dictionary	☐	☐
'oo' and 'ou' can both say /o͞o/	☐	☐
In 'slamming' doubling the 'm' keeps the 'a' short	☐	☐
In 'naming' the 'a' is short	☐	☐

SIGHT WORDS *Can you find these words? They may go like this ↓→ or like this ⤢ .*

board	once	tar		v	k	n	o	c	k	t	w	o
broad	pet	the		o	n	c	e	h	n	a	h	b
educate	push	there		s	o	l	d	i	e	r	e	e
here	put	toe		t	w	r	i	t	e	r	r	y
hit	resign	too		e	b	r	o	a	d	p	e	t
knee	roar	two		a	o	w	o	a	p	u	s	h
knock	saw	where		k	a	s	o	n	r	t	t	e
know	soldier	writer		s	r	e	s	i	g	n	o	r
obey	son	wrong		e	d	u	c	a	t	e	o	e
	steaks											

'oi', 'oy': /oy/

Note If a suffix comes after vowel + 'y', keep the 'y', e.g. t<u>oy</u>s.

> /**oy**/ is spelt '**oi**' in the **middle** of words, e.g. p**oi**nt, c**oi**ns.
>
> '**oy**' at the **end** of words, e.g. b**oy**, t**oy**.
>
> AND keep '**oy**' before **all** suffixes, e.g. empl**oy**ment, enj**oy**able.
>
> EXCEPTIONS with '**oy**' in the **middle**: v**oy**age, l**oy**al, r**oy**al, **oy**ster.

A COMPLETE these phrases with 'oi' or 'oy'.

a n _**oi**_ sy b _**oy**_

b___ling ___l

empl___ your brain

a strict empl____er

___ntment for cuts

deadly p___son

a l___al subject

the t___let block

enj___ing reading

a deep v___ce

a stiff j___nt

the r___al family

a sharp p___nt

av___d trouble

a long v___age

destr___ the baddies

rule RECAP

Use '___' in the middle of words.

Use '___' at the end of words and use '___' before a suffix.

B LOOK at this tongue twister, then try saying it fast:

A noisy noise annoys a noisy oyster.

How many times does 's' say /z/? _____

How many 'n's in 'annoys'? _____

Is the 's' in 'annoys' a suffix? _____

In which word is 'y' an exception to the rule? _____

Which word comes into the tongue twister twice? _____

C NOW COVER the tongue twister, WRITE it, then CHECK it.

_____

'ou', 'ow': /ow/ as in 'owl'

/**ow**/ can be spelt '**ou**' or '**ow**', e.g. l**ou**d sh**ou**t, br**ow**n **ow**l.

Note 'ou' also says /o͞o/, e.g. soup, 'ow' also says /ō/, e.g. crow.

The best way to decide whether /**ow**/ is '**ou**' or '**ow**' is to remember: **rhyming words** are spelt the **same way**, e.g. r**ou**nd m**ou**nd, d**ow**n t**ow**n.

A LEARN this memory jogger for 'ow' saying /ow/:

The owl in the tower saw a brown cow.

B USING the starter letters to help, LIST the 'ow' rhyming words:

owl	tower	brown	cow
f_____	fl_____	cr_____	v_____
gr_____	p_____	g_____	h_____
pr_____		fr_____	n_____
sc_____		dr_____	r_____
h_____		cl_____	all_____

C LEARN this memory jogger, then LIST the 'ou' rhyming words:

A round count of about 100 cars an hour go by.

round	count	about	hour
p_____	m_____	l_____	s_____
s_____	am_____	cl_____	fl_____
gr_____	acc_____	sh_____	
f_____	c_____y	sp_____	
b_____	f_____air	tr_____	

*rule*RE CAP _____

WRITE the two memory jogger sentences here.

_____

_____

'au', 'aw': /or/

Note 'or' and 'al' can also say /or/, e.g. stork, stalk.

> For /or/ use '**au**' **starting** or **mid-word**, e.g. **Au**gust, l**au**nch.
> Use '**aw**' ① to **end** a word, e.g. dr**aw**, l**aw**, s**aw**;
> ② before an '**-l**' or '**-n**' **ending**, e.g. cr**aw**l, y**aw**n.
> EXCEPTIONS: '**au**' in h**au**l (*pull*), '**aw**' in **aw**fully **aw**kward.

A ▶ *TRACK the 'aw' words here.*

With a yawn and a stretch, I got out of bed at dawn one raw cold morning and looked out of the window. I saw a jackdaw on the lawn trying to gnaw the meat off a bone that he had in his claw. He looked very awkward as he opened his jaw wide to get at all the meat.

B ▶ *FILL IN 'au' or 'aw' here.*

An _au_ thor was writing a story about a h____nted house. An outl____ had hidden there when he s____ an astron____t in the woods, bec____se he was afraid of being c____ght. The house was an ____ful place. Rats had tried to gn____ a hole in the door, and piles of str____, old l____ndry, sh____ls, broken s____cers and rubbish covered the floor. The astron____t had not seen the outl____. He was looking for a f____lt in his l____nch pad which had c____sed a long p____se before his last d____n flight.

👁👁 **SIGHT WORDS** awkward, daughter, laughter.
For irregular words, try saying th[...]ps of 2 or 3,
 e.g. aw kw ard [...] er daughter.
Now COVER, WRITE _____ AND check.

TRACK the 'aught' words here.
He traced his naughty daughter by her la[...], and he caught her.

Strengthen Your Spelling. Copyright © 1996 Elizabeth Wood. Published by Hodder & Stoughton Educational. The publishers grant permission for copies of this sheet to be made in the purchasing school or college for use solely in that institution.

'ie': /ē/, /ī/, /ĕ/

'ie' breaks the usual rule which says:

'When two vowels go out walking the first one does the talking'

> 'ie' says /ē/, e.g. sh**ie**ld, th**ie**f, n**ie**ce, f**ie**rce.
> EXCEPTIONS: 'ie' says /ī/ in p**ie**, d**ie**, l**ie**, t**ie** ;
> and /ĕ/ in fr**ie**nd.

 A TRACK the 'ie' words here.

After a fierce fight, the city was besieged.

The enemy chief said, "This city is short

of water and will have to yield very soon."

Inside the city the priest was saying, "Friends, I will be brief. To

grieve over this will achieve nothing. Keep your swords and shields ready,

but believe with me that relief will come." That night it rained and every

piece of crockery in the city was filled with water.

 B LINK these starters to their endings, then WRITE the word.

pr	ield	*field*
f	iece	_____
be	ief	_____
p	lief	_____
th	iest	_____

ch	iege	_____
s	lieve	_____
a	riek	_____
sh	ief	_____
re	chieve	_____

C PUT some of these words into a sentence: tie, lie, die, pie.

_____

*rule*RECAP

'ie' usually says /___/.

'ei': /ā/, /ē/, /ī/, /ĕ/

'ei' can say /ā/, e.g. **ei**ght, sl**ei**gh , r**ei**ndeer;
/ē/, e.g. c**ei**ling, prot**ei**n, s**ei**ze, rec**ei**ve, w**ei**rd.
EXCEPTIONS: 'ei' says /ī/ in h**ei**ght, either, neither, and /ĕ/ in l**ei**sure.

A You will need these words to solve this puzzle:

ceiling	neither
deceives	receive
eight	reign
eighty	rein
foreign	their
height	vein
neigh	weighs
neighbours	weird

ACROSS

1 Strange or odd.
5 Two times four.
7 From another country.
9 Cry like a horse.
10 To accept something given.
12 Finds the heaviness of.
14 People living nearby.
15 One more than 79.
16 A strap for leading a horse.

DOWN

2 Misleads by telling lies.
3 A king's _____ is when he rules.
4 Belonging to them.
6 Distance from bottom to top.
8 Not one or the other.
11 The inner roof of a room.
13 A tube carrying blood.

B CIRCLE the silent letters in each word, then COVER and WRITE the word.

weight (*heaviness*), sleigh (*sledge*), receipt (*for money paid*),

heir (*to the throne*), freight (*cargo*).

/er/: er, ir, ur

Spelling the sound /er/:

> **'er'** is the most usual /er/ **ending** e.g. thund**er**, matt**er**,
>   but it can come mid-word, e.g. n**er**ve, t**er**m, f**er**n
> **'ur'** is the most usual spelling **mid-word**,
>   e.g. ch**ur**ch, m**ur**der, Th**ur**sday.
> **'ir'** is used for **numbers** and **mid-word**, e.g. th**ir**ty, b**ir**ds

The easiest way to remember these spellings is to group them together.

A *TRACK the 'ir' words here, then LIST them below.*

The first girl had a T-shirt which was dirty,

The third was like a bird, and always thirsty,

The thirteenth in a skirt was rather flirty,

But the boss was very firm with all the thirty.

_____

_____

B *Now TRACK and LIST the 'ur' words here.*

"But surgeon, this is urgent," said the nurse,

"This very disturbed patient makes me curse,

She's hurt her hand, she's burned it

On a saucepan as she turned it,

And now she says 'In church I've lost my purse'."

_____

_____

UNSCRAMBLE these words: f m i r *__firm___*, u n r b _____,

v e s e r _____, s i t r _____, d u r e r m _____,

e r n v e _____.

/er/: er, ir, ur; the sounds of 'ear'

> 'ear' can say: ① /er/, e.g. **ear**th, s**ear**ch, h**ear**d;
>
> ② /**ear**/, e.g. **ear**, cl**ear**, d**ear**, n**ear**;
>
> ③ /**air**/, e.g. b**ear**, p**ear**, t**ear**-away;
>
> ④ /**ar**/, e.g. h**ear**t, h**ear**th, h**ear**ty.

A *USE these 'ear' words to FILL the spaces:*

bear, clearing, early, hearty, learn, near, rears, rehearsal.

Len _____ sheep in a _____ _____ here.

_____ this and come _____ to the _____.

I can't _____ that man. He is too _____ for me.

B *TICK pairs of rhyming words*   learn

then WRITE them down.   nerve   thirst

FIND the odd word.   girl   swear   batters

thirty   furnish   hears   birds

burned   surprise   hurls   earn   thirds

bear   patters   first   dirty

burnish   serve   curls

fears   turned

swirl

_____ _____   _____ _____

_____ _____   _____ _____

_____ _____   _____ _____

_____ _____   _____ _____

_____ _____   _____ _____

_____   _____

The odd word is _____

sYs 39.2

More about commas ─────────────────────────

Punctuation marks are used to make a sentence easier to read.

Note A **comma**, indicating where to pause, is used:

① to replace '**and**' in **lists** of words, phrases and **linked** sentences,

② **before** and **after interruptions**, e.g. Tom**,** our cat**,** is very old.

A **comma** also

③ marks the **end** of an **aside** (interruption) at the start of a sentence,
e.g. Although she is tired**,** Mary is swimming well;

④ marks a pause for breath between two **long, linked** sentences,
e.g. I hoped that I would be in time to catch the last bus**,** so that I
would not have to spend money on a taxi.

A PUT one comma into each of these sentences.

Without thinking where he was going David took the wrong turning.

He had left home in very good time but he was late for his appointment.

We did not go away on holiday this year but we went out every day.

After eating a hasty breakfast Tim ran all the way to school.

B TICK the sentence which is punctuated correctly in each set.

The manager said, My secretary, Miss Smith, will write to you. ☐

The manager said, ''My secretary Miss Smith will write to you''. ☐

The manager said, ''My secretary, Miss Smith, will write to you.'' ☐

''Did you hear what I said?'' ☐

''did you hear what I said?'' ☐

''Did you hear what I said.'' ☐

Wearing his football kit Ali got on his bike, and went to the park. ☐

Wearing his football kit, Ali got on his bike and went to the park. ☐

Wearing his football kit Ali got on his bike and went to the park. ☐

The farmer's dog is a good watchdog, but it's no good with sheep. ☐

The farmer's dog is a good watchdog, But it's no good with sheep. ☐

The farmers' dog is a good watchdog, but its no good with sheep. ☐

Revision

Tick 'yes' or 'no' to these questions:

Would you just add the vowel suffix '-ing' to:

1 rain – yes(y) no(t)   **2** rub – yes(r) no(o)   **3** hurt – yes(u) no(y)

Would you drop 'e' before adding 'able' to:

4 love – yes(a) no(o)   **5** slice – yes(n) no(r)   **6** forge – yes(e) no(e)

Would you double the last consonant before adding 'ed' to:

7 lick – yes(m) no(b)   **8** slip – yes(r) no(o)   **9** seem – yes(r) no(i)

Would you change 'y' to 'i' before adding 'ed' to:

10 try – yes(l) no(e)   **11** toy – yes(-) no(l)   **12** empty – yes(i) no(t)

Would you change 'fe' or 'f' to 'ves' to make a plural of:

13 wife – yes(a) no(i)   **14** roof – yes(m) no(n)   **15** leaf – yes(t) no(e)

FILL in the letters that you have ticked, to get a message here:

1	2	3

4	5	6

7	8	9	10	11	12	13	14	15

Which word comes first in a dictionary 'steak' or 'steam'? _____

Does 'ea' say /ē/ or /ĕ/ in 'health', meant, sweater? /___/.

Cross out the wrong word in 'That team are/is brilliant'.

SIGHT WORDS REVISION *Only the first 1 or 2 letters differ in these pairs, but the words may not rhyme. WRITE the pairs and the odd word here:*

design
coarse   daughter   broad
height   awkward   road   hoarse   break
steak   resign   laughter
weight

_____ _____
_____ _____
_____ _____
_____ _____
_____ _____
_____ _____

The odd word is _____

Syllables: division ────────────────────────

Every **syllable** has **1 vowel sound**: i.e. **1 vowel**, **2 vowels** together, or **'y'**.

 A *FILL IN the missing vowels in this story.*

There w**a**s a n**o**tice on the g__te of an empt__ b__ngalow

say__ng 'D__NGER KE__P OUT'. S__me

ch__ldren w__nted to __xplore and

went to look in the w__ndows.

S__ddenly the earth start__d to sh__dder.

"R__n," Rupa shout__d to his s__ster.

"There is a coal m__ne __nder here."

As th__y ran away the bung__low f__ll

into a h__ge c__vern which h__d

__pened up, but the children were s__fe.

The vowels in syllable words are separated by 1 or 2 consonants.

Divide a word into syllables **before 1 consonant** or **between 2**.

B *FIND the vowels, then divide these words into syllables like this:*

p a | p e r ____*pā per*____   l e s s o n _____

p e n c i l _____   b r o k e n _____

d e n t i s t _____   s i s t e r _____

h a p p e n _____   s i l e n t _____

s t u d e n t _____   p o n y _____

MARK each of the first syllable vowels like this: long ‾ *or short* ˘.

Are the long or the short vowels followed by two consonants? _____

*rule*RECAP _____

Every syllable must have a _____ or '__'
Divide a word into syllables _____ 1 consonant or _____ 2.

 sYs 42.1

Syllables: open and closed

Note A long vowel says its name: ā, ē, ī, ō, ū.

> A **closed** syllable ends with a **consonant**, and the vowel is **short**.
>   e.g. răb/bĭt, pĕn/cĭl, ĭn/sĕct.
> An **open** syllable ends with a **vowel** and the vowel is **long**.
>   e.g. pō/ny, bā/ker, spī/der.

A MARK the vowels in these starter syllables **long** ⁻ or **short** ˘.

com-, con-, de-, e-, ex-, im-, pre-, sub-, trans-.

B Now USE these starter syllables to make three words with each ending.

press   vent   mit

port   tract   tend

Note Divide into syllables in front of 1 consonant or between 2.

C DIVIDE these words into syllables.

baker **ba / ker**   unit ____/____

envy ____/____   hundred ____/____

lesson ____/____   begin ____/____

pilot ____/____   decide ____/____

human ____/____   letter ____/____

insect ____/____   transfer ____/____

rule RECAP _____

> An **open** syllable ends with a _____.
> A **closed** syllable ends with a _____.

Syllables: open and closed

Note An **open** syllable ends with a **vowel** and the vowel is **long**; a **closed** syllable ends with a **consonant** and the vowel is **short**.

A *In each block, one of these starter syllables will make a word with all of the given endings:* con-, coun-, dis-, pro-, re-, trans-.

```
                gress              gret              cil
_____ <----- long      _____ <----- vise      _____ <----- ter
                vide               ward              ty


                cern               cover             fer
_____ <----- tain      _____ <----- trict      _____ <----- mit
                vict               tance             port
```

B *Use these endings and COMPLETE this news flash:*
-cern, -cil, -der, -dren, gret, -nance, -port, -raid, -tance, -teen, -ty, -vide.

The con**cern**_____ of the coun_____ is to pro_____

trans_____ for the chil_____ un_____ thir_____

who live a long dis_____ from their school, but the fi_____

officer said, "I re_____ having to say this, but I'm af_____

there is no cash in the kit_____."

C *In a dictionary, which words completed in B would be between these words?*

circle – divide _____

face – knee _____

prowl – trap _____

Syllables: division of irregular words _____

Sometimes a short vowel is **not** protected by two consonants.

Note Never use 'v v', i.e. ne**v**er, le**v**el, de**v**il, ci**v**ic.

> There is only one consonant between two 'i's, e.g. ri**g**id, li**m**it, di**g**it.
> *Remember:* You only have one nose between two eyes.

Remember other irregular words by learning the sound pattern,
   like this: rŏb/in,   měn/u,   lěm/on.

> 'ia', 'io' and at times 'ie' **are 2 syllables**. Divide **i/a**, **i/o**, **i/e**,
>   e.g. zo/di/ac,   ra/di/o,   di/et,   sci/ence,   a/li/ens.

A ▶ *TRY both a short and a long vowel for the first syllables here:*
e.g. prŏv/ide prō/vide,   fĭn/al fī/nal,   răp/id rā/pid.
When you find a word, divide the syllables like this:

p r o f/i t	r o b i n	m e t a l	s t u d e n t
a/c o r n	l i o n	l i m i t	q u i e t
m o t o r	r a d a r	f i n a l	f i n i s h
r o b o t	n e v e r	d i e t	c r e d i t
d a m a g e	d i a l	s p i d e r	s t a t i c

B ▶ *DRAW lines between syllables to make words, then WRITE them.*

van	bot	*robot* _____	stu	ic	_____
spi	age	_____	cred	nal	_____
lim	gent	_____	stat	al	_____
dam	ish	_____	met	vil	_____
ro	der	_____	fi	it	_____
a	it	_____	e	dent	_____

ruleRECAP _____
> There is only _____ consonant between 2 '_____'s.

sYs
42.4

Syllables: multi-syllable words

> To find syllables, divide **all** words **before** 1 consonant or **between** 2,
>   e.g. but/ter/fly, ac/ro/bat, chim/pan/zee;
> OR **after** 1 consonant, if the vowel before it is short, e.g. lĕm/on/ade.

A *DIVIDE the words:* i n d u s t r y,   r e m e m b e r,   v i n e g a r,   p u n i s h m e n t,   a d v e n t u r e,   f a n t a s t i c.

B *SOLVE this crossword puzzle. To help with the clues, there are jumbled syllables for the syllable words, and jumbled letters in CAPITALS for some of the other words.*

ACROSS

1 dile o croc – River animal.

7 vent pre – Hinder.

8 E A D R – Loved.

10 Not 'yes'.

11 ven e – Level, smooth.

14 vise re – Learn again.

15 More rare.

17 S T V E – Animal doctors.

18 Not cold.

19 ree ag – To say 'yes'.

21 ger ti – Indian animal.

23 A R G U D – To keep safe.

24 To chew and swallow food.

25 – er deaf – More deaf.

27 D R M E A – Seen when asleep.

28 O D – To work at.

29 ed it – Prepare for printing.

DOWN

1 per cop – A reddish metal.

2 er o pen – Use to unfasten.

3 ver o – Above.

4 ed ter in est – Being curious about.

5 en dive – A sort of lettuce.

6 port trans ed – Carried.

9 O E R – Fishes' eggs.

12 van guard – Front of the army.

13 er nev – At no time

16 E D E R – A tall stiff grass.

18 Pronoun for a man.

19 A D E G – Old.

20 A R T E – The speed of things.

22 ant gi – A very big man.

26 Go bad.

Suffixes: the doubling rule on multi-syllable words _____

Note On a one-syllable word ending 1 vowel + 1 consonant, **double** the **consonant** before adding a **vowel** suffix, e.g. skip + ing = ski**pp**ing.

When adding a **vowel** suffix to a base word with two or more syllables, **only double** the consonant after **1 (short) vowel** when:

① the **stress** is on the **last** syllable of the base word,

e.g. forgét + ing = forgétting,   BUT límit + ed = límited;

or ② the word ends with **1 vowel + 'l'** wherever the stress,

e.g. quárrel + ed = quárrelled,   contról + ed = contrólled.

A FINDING the stress. Say 'differ' stressing '**dif**', like this: **díf**fer

Say 'prefer' stressing '**fer**', like this: pre**fér**

TAP out these words and mark the stressed syllable like this: númber

scatter,   occur,   gallop,   begin,   acquit,   offer,   button,   forget

B *Look back at the rule, then ADD 'ed' to these base words.*

cancel **led**　　　　occur_____　　　　offer_____

credit_____　　　　prefer_____　　　　travel_____

regret_____　　　　limit_____　　　　equip_____

patrol_____　　　　suffer_____　　　　label_____

differ_____　　　　acquit_____　　　　whisper_____

*rule*RE**CAP** _____

On multi-syllable words, only use the doubling rule before a vowel suffix:

if the _____ is on the last syllable, or the word ends 1 vowel + '____'.

Inverted commas and indirect speech

 Note Inverted **commas** mark the beginning and end of **direct speech** (spoken words), e.g. The teacher said, ''Ben is lazy.''

Notice: **inverted commas – capital letter – full stop – inverted commas.**

> Inverted commas are **not** used when something that has been said is being reported later. This is called **indirect** or **reported speech**,
>
>   e.g. The teacher told me that Ben was lazy.

A ▶ *WRITE what these people are saying, in indirect (reported) speech.*

Gemma said that _____

Dawn told me _____

Alex insisted that _____

but Ali said that _____

> Other uses of **inverted commas** are the marking of:
>
> ① the **beginning** and **end** of quotations,
>
>   e.g. Proverbially ''All work and no play makes Jack a dull boy'';
>
> ② **titles** of books, films, plays, etc.
>
>   e.g. Shakespeare's play ''The Merchant of Venice''...;
>
> ③ a **foreign** word or a word **out of** its usual **context**,
>
>   e.g. That was a dreadful mistake, a real ''faux pas'',
>
>   or Jim said that he ''accidentally'' spilt the medicine.

B ▶ *PUNCTUATE this.*

david said james said that hed lend me jason and the bandits then

hell lend it to you said davids mum james always keeps his word

Revision

To SOLVE this CROSSWORD, choose the right spelling in each clue. Use the rules you know. When in doubt, USE a DICTIONARY.

ACROSS

1 emploiing employing
6 exppres express
7 stay stai
8 lever lev ver
12 rowd rode
13 it itt
15 file fille
17 prikked pricked
18 rim rimm
20 roum room
21 gided guided
22 pipe piep

DOWN

1 ever ev ver
2 peper pepper
3 openned opened
4 goat gowt
5 plaied played
7 soil soyl
9 voice voise
10 refer reffer
11 hopeing hoping
14 tirm term
16 idoll idol
19 male malle

Word endings: /l/: '-le'

> **Before** adding the ending '-**le**' to a single syllable, you need:
> 1. **two** consonants after a **short vowel**, e.g. pa**dd**le;
> 2. **one** consonant after a **long** vowel or vowel + vowel (**v v**), e.g. ta**b**le, nee**d**le.

A ADD '-le' to the starting letters below. If you <u>need</u> an extra consonant after a <u>short</u> vowel, **double** the last consonant.

rif... *rifle*   ang..._____   lit..._____

simp..._____   bib..._____   feeb..._____

bot..._____   tumb..._____   tit..._____

doub..._____   mid..._____   raf..._____

mud..._____   troub..._____   cand..._____

B TRACK the words ending '-le' or '-les', then CORRECT them if they are wrongly spelt.

Some people were trying to smugle some rare plants out of the junggle. It was no simple task. They had to batle against beettles, mosquitos, and bramble-like creepers that tried to stranggle them. There were netles that stung them, and once they met a rattlesnake in the midle of their path which they had to shoot with their riffle. To cap it all, at the airport, their bundles of rare plants, hidden under their dufle coats, were confiscated.

*rule*RECAP

> Before an '-le' ending, after one syllable, there should be:
> 2 consonants after a _____ vowel,
> and 1 consonant after a _____ vowel or vowel + _____.

Strengthen Your Spelling. Copyright © 1996 Elizabeth Wood. Published by Hodder & Stoughton Educational. The publishers grant permission for copies of this sheet to be made in the purchasing school or college for use solely in that institution.

Word endings: /l/: '-al' and '-el' _____

> The letters S, U, R, M, N, W, and V never take an '-le' ending.
> *Remember:* **S**imon's **U**ncle **R**oger **M**akes **N**ice **W**arm **V**ests.
> 's' is followed by '**-tle**', e.g. thi**stle**, ca**stle** .
> '**u**', '**r**', '**m**', '**n**', '**w**' and '**v**' are followed by '**-al**' or '**-el**',
>   e.g. sign**al**, anim**al**, trow**el**, nov**el**.

A *STORE the spelling of the words below in a <u>sound</u> form in your mind, by pronouncing the endings /ăl/ or /ĕl/ as you read them.*

U	R	M	N	W	V
individ**u**al	gene**r**al	deci**m**al	chan**n**el	to**w**el	ri**v**al
us**u**al	cathed**r**al	ani**m**al	tun**n**el	vo**w**el	tra**v**el
act**u**al	cent**r**al	dis**m**al	origi**n**al	je**w**el	no**v**el
eq**u**al	seve**r**al	ca**m**el	fi**n**al	tro**w**el	mar**v**el

B *FILL IN '-al' or '-el' in the spaces (in each sentence, all the gaps need '-al' or all need '-el').*

We can trav**el** by train through the Chann_____ Tunn_____, but, in the

desert, men trav_____ on cam_____s.

In actu_____ fact, every anim_____ is an individu_____.

The decim_____ .3 is equ_____ to 3/10.

The vow_____s in 'tow_____' and 'jew_____' are 'o' and 'e'.

The cathedr_____ and sever_____ shops are in the centr_____ square.

C *Can you SORT OUT these anagrams? The words are in the lists above.*

l u u a s _____   f l i n a _____   e n l v o _____

rule RECAP ...._____

> Except in 'hassle', these letters are never followed by an '-le' ending:
> _____, _____, _____, _____, _____, _____, _____,
> 's' is followed by '_____'   e.g. whistle.

Word endings: /l/: /kl/: revision

Note You need **2** consonants between a **short** vowel and a final '**-le**'.

> A /**kl**/ ending is: '**ckle**' after a **short vowel**, e.g. knu**ckle**s,
> '**kle**' after **vowel + consonant**, e.g. an**kle**, spar**kle**.

A few words end '**-cle**', not '-kle'. Remember them like this:
It was a mira**cle**. Without his specta**cle**s, Un**cle** cy**cle**d in cir**cle**s round trea**cle**
tins and other arti**cle**s in an obsta**cle** race.

A ▶ CHECK *whether the vowel is short, then ADD a* /kl/ *ending here.*

ta _ckle_   un_____   sprin_____   cy_____

chu_____   arti_____   spar_____   cir_____

obsta_____   bu_____   cra_____   twin____

B ▶ **RULE BREAKERS.** *Say these words, pronouncing them as they are written:*
hos-pit-al, pet-al, cryst-al, tot-al, la-bel, reb-el, mus-cle.
Try to VISUALISE two of them written high on a wall in colour.

C ▶ FILL IN *the right endings where the '-le', '-al' and '-el' tracks cross.*

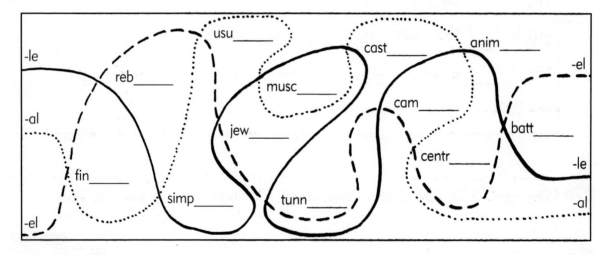

usu_____   cast_____   anim_____

-le

reb_____   musc_____

-el

-al   jew_____   cam_____   batt_____

fin_____   centr_____   -le

simp_____   tunn_____   -al

-el

Did you fill in each ending four times?

> Usually a /kl/ ending after a short vowel is '_____',
> and after a vowel + consonant is '_____'.

Word endings: /er/ and /cher/

A ▶ *FIND your own rules. The endings of the words below sound like /er/.*
SORT them into lists with the same endings:

neighbour, dollar, colour, actor, finger, flavour, collar, river, editor, better, winter, doctor, popular, muscular, operator, rubber, dictator, rumour, packer, singular, harbour, professor, regular, labour, particular, aggressor, armour, hammer.

'-ar'	'-or'	'-er'	'-our'
____	____	____	____
____	____	____	____
____	____	____	____
____	____	____	____
____	____	____	____
____	____	____	____
____	____	____	____
		____	

B ▶ *COMPLETE this rule box.*

> Use '____' after 'l',
>
> Use '____' after 'at', 'ct', 'it' and 'ess'.
>
> Use '____' to end neighbour, armour, harbour and abstract nouns.
>
> But when in doubt, use the most common /er/ ending '____'.

> The ending sounding like /**cher**/ is spelt '**-ture**', e.g. cap**ture**, vul**ture**.

C ▶ *TRACK '-ture' endings here.*

At the Car Boot Sale there was a real mixture of books on show. There were adventure stories, and picture books, nature study and scripture books, literature for culture, and strange tales of future creatures.

Word endings: /shŭn/ after a vowel _____

For the ending /**shŭn**/ after a **vowel** use:

'-**ssion**' after **short** /ă/, /ĕ/ and /ŭ/, and for words ending '-**mission**',

e.g. proc**ĕssion**, disc**ŭssion**, per**mission**;

'-**tion**' after **long vowels** and often **short** /ĭ/ (not 'mission'),

e.g. irrit**ātion**, compl**ētion**, oppos**ĭtion**.

A *FIND the hidden word. TURN these verbs into a noun ending with '-tion'.*

Add...
Create...
Dictate...
Propose...
Circulate...
Examine...
Determine...
Imitate...
Promote...
Sense...

You deserve a *_____* (a medal). Well done!

B *FILL IN '-ssion' or '-tion' endings here.*

Have you got permi**ssion** to go on this expedi_____?

The discu_____ about the competi_____ for jobs was good.

In that loca_____ the TV transmi_____ is poor.

Your ambi_____ shows in your devo_____ to your job.

In good acting, the expre_____ of emo_____ is important.

The man made a confe_____ of his posse_____ of drugs.

rule RECAP _____

Use '_____' after short 'a', 'e' and 'u' and /mĭ/, Use '_____'
after a long vowel or short 'i' except in 'mission'.

sYs
48.1

Word endings: /shŭn/ after a consonant; /zyŭn/ '-sion'

The sound **/shŭn/** after a **consonant** is usually '-**tion**',
   e.g. frac**tion**,   direc**tion**.
BUT in the words below, /**shŭn**/ after a **consonant** is spelt '-**sion**':

tension	version	emulsion	mansion
extension	conversion	compulsion	expansion
comprehension	immersion	propulsion	

A *SORT these syllables into words:*   sion ten ex ___*extension*___

tion ac re _____   la u tion pop _____

mul sion e _____   po si tion com _____

pul sion pro _____   tion ten at _____

The sound **/zyŭn/** after a **vowel** is spelt '-**sion**',
   e.g. explo**sion**,   televi**sion** .

B *ADD '-sion' or '-tion' to these starter letters. Find the whole word, then listen for /zyŭn/ or /shŭn/.*

revi ***sion*** ___   igni_____   mo_____   explo_____

occa_____   ero_____   ambi_____   fu_____

divi_____   sta_____   conclu_____   educa_____

C *TRACK '-sion' words in one colour, '-tion' words in a different colour.*

Did I mention that an extension is to be added to the old mansion? This

means a revision of my plans for the conversion of my garage to an extra

reception room. No action has been taken yet, but tension is mounting. I

want to avoid friction if I can, but I may have no option.

*rule*RE CAP _____

/zyŭn/ is spelt '_____'

/shŭn/ after a consonant is usually '_____'.

Mid-word /**sh**/ is spelt '**ci**' or '**ti**', e.g. spe**ci**al pa**ti**ent.

Sometimes a root word will show you whether to use 'ci' or 'ti',

   e.g. gra**c**e gra**ci**ous,   confiden**t** confiden**ti**al.

Only use '**sh**' mid-word in mu**sh**room,   cu**sh**ion,   fa**sh**ion.

A *A few words derived from Greek take a '-cian' ending, e.g. technician.*
The expert in optics *is an op*ti*cian. Who are the experts in:*

magic _____   music _____   physics _____

electrics _____   politics _____

B *ADD '-ous' /us/ or '-al' /ŭl/ after 'ci' or 'ti' /sh/ in these phrases.*

preci **ous**___ stone;   confidenti_____ letter;   a vici_____ animal;

soci_____ history;   artifici_____ limb;   initi_____ letters;

essenti_____ ingredient;   delici_____ sweet;   very suspici_____.

ruleRE CAP

Mid-word '____' and '____' say /sh/. Only use 'sh' in:

_____   _____   _____

RULE QUIZ 11 ??

Is 'ia' in 'dial' and 'io' in 'riot' 1 or 2 syllables? _____

Is the stress in 'limit' on the last syllable? _____

Do you double 'l' before adding a vowel suffix to 'quarrel'? _____

What is the sound of 'ei' in 'protein', 'seize', and 'receive'? /___/

The letters which do not take an '-le' ending are S U R M __ __ __

How do you spell /shun/ after short 'a', 'e' or 'u'? _____

How do you spell /zyun/ at the end of a word? _____

Would you expect to find an '-ar' ending after 'l'? _____

What is the most common /er/ ending? '_____'

When do you end with '-or'? After ___t, ___t, ___t and ___ ___s.

How many consonants do you need between a short vowel and 'le'? _____

Punctuation revision _____

A ANSWER *these quiz questions with the appropriate punctuation marks.*

_____ shows exactly where a letter or letters have been omitted.

_____ shows that the speaker or writer is expecting an answer.

___ and ___ mark the beginning and end of spoken words.

_____ replaces 'and' in lists of words or phrases.

_____ marks the end of a sentence.

_____ between the owner(s) and 's' shows possession.

_____ shows where you need to pause when reading a sentence.

___ and ___ are always in pairs.

_____ tells you to read a word or sentence with much feeling.

_____ is followed by a capital letter.

B PUNCTUATE *this story.*

a conjurer rick had been invited to tonys birthday party but tony was worried

he had a £10 note which he had no intention of losing tucked into his

jacket pocket

who is going to help me the conjurer asked and looking round the

room he pointed his wand at tony

thats my man he said id like the lad

with ginger hair blue eyes and glasses

tony had no option shaking with fright

he walked forward and rick shook him firmly by the hand tony was looking

fearfully at ricks wand his lighter and an ash tray throwing tony a big ball

rick said stand back tony catch this as tony caught the ball it split open

inside was a £10 note tony grinned i thought youd like that back rick said

and heres another note for your birthday all tony could say was wow

Silent letters

Because the pronunciation of words has changed over the years, some words are spelt with letters which are no longer sounded, e.g. <u>w</u>ho.

A *CIRCLE or colour the silent (unsounded) letters in these words.*

autumn	iron	hour	crumb
ghost	whose	guard	knot
honest	column	limb	fasten
descend	half	dialogue	vehicle
climb	answer	know	solemn
island	scent	condemn	whole

B *Can you FILL these gaps? In each sentence all the gaps need the same silent letter. You will need: b, c, g, h, k, n, s, t, w.*

Jo created a s*c*ene in s__ience because she needed some s__issors.

_hose is this s__ord with the ancient __riting on it?

Guy ran a campai__n to advertise a new desi__n for garden __nomes.

I __new the __night had __nocked his __nee and lost his __nife.

He was ex__austed so the c__emist gave him some g__astly medicine.

I dou__t whether I can settle my de__t with the plum__er this week.

The judge was very solem__ as he said "I condem__ this man to death."

I shouted from the boat but there was no answer from the i__land.

If you lis__en you can of__en hear the whis__le of the fast train.

Silent letters: 'gh' in 'augh' and 'ough' _____

> 'gh' is silent or says /f/ in 'ough', e.g. d**ough** /ō/,   c**ough** /ŏf/.

Use the sound clues to help you read this memory jogger (mnemonic):

To learn o-u-g-h is tough /ŭf/

There's though /ō/ and through /o͞o/ and trough /ŏf/ and rough /ŭf/

And thought /ort/ and fought /ort/ and bough /ow/ and cough /ŏf/,

And brought /ort/ and bought /ort/ and plough /ow/ and trough /ŏf/

"Enough /ŭf/, enough /ŭf/," I hear you cry,

"That's thorough /ŭ-rŭ/ enough /ŭf/," and so say I.

A *Use these 'ough' words to FILL IN the spaces below:*
ought, bought, brought, thought, though, thorough.

_____ Dad has just _____

a computer for me, Mum _____ that I

_____ to have a _____

spring-clean, before anything else is _____

into my room. Perhaps... Mum is right.

> 'augh' says /or/, e.g. c**augh**t,   d**augh**ter,
> except in l**augh** and dr**augh**t where it may say /arf/ or /af/.

B *Unscramble the letters to find words with 'aught' in them.*

Captured ... h a c g u t   ___*caught*___

Given a lesson ... t g a h t u   _____

Badly behaved ... t a h g u n y   _____

Someone's female child ... a d g h u r t e   _____

The sound of a laugh ... g l e a t h u r   _____

Cold air blowing into a room ... u r g d a t h   _____

The killing of many animals or people ... s e h a u l g t r   _____

sYs
51.2

'ph' saying /f/

In words of Greek origin, **'ph'** says /**f**/, e.g. gra**ph** ,   hy**ph**en.

A *COLOUR MARK 'ph' in these words, READ them, then FIND the underlined words in the WORDSEARCH square, written in these directions.*

alphabet	pharmacy	a	m	p	h	i	b	i	a	n	t
amphibian	phase	l	t	r	i	u	m	p	h	e	e
atmosphere	Philip	p	y	m	w	c	o	h	t	p	l
autograph	phonic	h	p	o	o	g	r	a	p	h	e
decipher	phosphate	a	h	d	r	s	h	s	f	e	p
dolphin	photograph	b	o	g	i	p	p	e	k	w	h
elephant	phrase	e	o	l	s	h	h	h	m	o	a
emphasize	physical	t	n	o	q	e	r	a	e	s	n
geography	physics	u	h	x	v	r	b	l	n	r	t
graph	prophet	p	t	e	l	e	p	h	o	n	e
hyphen	sphere										
nephew	telegraph										
orphan	telephone										
paragraph	triumph										
phantom	typhoon										

B *ANSWER these clues with a word from the list above.*

A picture taken with a camera _____.

A sea creature like a porpoise _____.

The air round the earth _____.

An animal that lives on land and in water _____.

Someone who foretells what he thinks will happen _____.

To stress certain words when speaking _____.

A small group of words _____..

To turn a coded message into ordinary writing _____.

An instrument for speaking to someone far away _____.

The study of different parts of the world _____.

A salt of phosphorus, a soil fertilizer _____.

A branch of science _____.

Homophones _____

> **Homophones** are words which sound the same,
> but have **different spellings** for **different meanings**,
>   e.g. I must **warn** you that the brakes on that bike are **worn** out.

A *USING a dictionary, circle the word which matches each definition.*

Belonging to them...	their there	To throw away as useless...	waist waste
To interfere with...	medal meddle	Freedom from war...	peace piece
Part of your foot...	heal heel	Used to slow a car down...	brake break
A colour...	blue blew	Past tense of 'catch'...	caught court
Heaviness...	weight wait	Where something happens...	scene seen
Something learned...	lessen lesson	To discover something...	find fined

B *FILL the gaps with the words from the box.*

wood would	
wear where	
shore sure	
hour our	
hear here	
weak week	
son sun	
heard herd	
hole whole	
for four	

I _____ get some _____ for you if I could.

_____ could I _____ a jacket like that?

I'm _____ I saw a seal on the sea_____

_____ school play starts in one _____'s time.

If you stand _____ you may _____ the cuckoo.

I felt _____ for a _____ when I had the 'flu.

Len's _____ got badly _____ burnt today.

Have you _____? I have sold my _____ of cows.

My _____ foot went into the _____ in my sock.

Is there enough ice-cream _____ _____ of us?

Puzzle answers

2.5

C	R	I	S	P	S		A	
H			T			H	A	N G
O V E R			I		D O T		
P			I S N T				
	B A N K			H A N D		
W E		G I V E			U	
E		O	P E N			M	
E N D			T		T A P		
K		D I N		C O T		

5.1

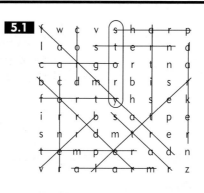

12

	Y O U				A T	
		U		F	C		H E
W A T E R		O		E
H			I		M A N Y
A	W H E R E		A M
T		N		M
	S A I D		D O E S
	O N		O S

14.2

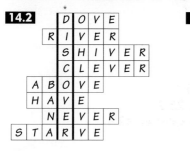

D O V E / R I V E R / S H I V E R / C L E V E R / A B O V E / H A V E / N E V E R / S T A R V E

15

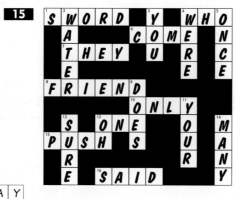

S W O R D / WHO / COME / THEY / SOURCE / FRIEND / ONLY / SONE / PUSH / SAID / MANY

23.2

SAY / SLAY / LAY / STAY / PLAY / STRAY / PRAY / TRAY

23.2

WEIGHT / REIN / VEIN / NEIGH / EIGHT / STRAIGHT / REIGN / FOREIGN

18

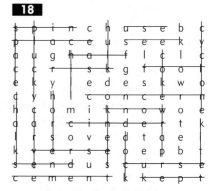

30.2

I	C	Y
M	A	K E R
P	L	A N N I N G
R	O	B B E R
O	I	L I N G
V	I	C E S
I	T	C H I N G
N	I	C E S T
G	R	I P P E D

33

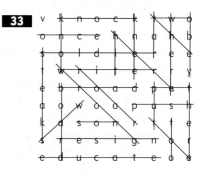

38

Across/Down answers:
WEIRD / EIGHT / FOREIGN / NEIGH / RECEIVE / WEIGHS / NEIGHBOURS / EIGHTY / REIN

42.5

CROCODILE / PREVENT / DEAR / NO / EVEN / REVISE / RARER / VETS / HOT / AGREE / TIGER / GUARD / EAT / DEAFER / DREAM / DO / EDIT

45

EMPLOYING / EXPRESS / STAY / LEVER / RODE / IT / FILE / PRICKED / RIM / ROOM / GUIDED / PIPE

48.1

| A D D I T I O N |
| C R E A T I O N |
| D I C T A T I O N |
| P R O P O S I T I O N |
| C I R C U L A T I O N |
| E X A M I N A T I O N |
| D E T E R M I N A T I O N |
| I M I T A T I O N |
| P R O M O T I O N |
| S E N S A T I O N |

52

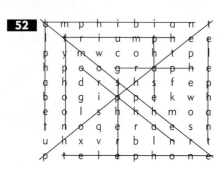

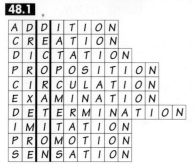

Index

Index _(continued)

Sight Words